THE DXCC COMPANION

By Jim Kearman, KR1S

**Published by
The American Radio Relay League
225 Main Street, Newington, CT 06111**

Cover:
Steve Mansfield, N1MZA, and his daughter
Elizabeth share the excitement of some DX
QSL cards.

Table of Contents

Preface

Chapter 1	What is DXing?	7
Chapter 2	Who are These DXers, Anyway?	13
Chapter 3	What Do I Need to Be a DXer?	17
Chapter 4	Getting Organized	27
Chapter 5	Your First DX Contact	37
Chapter 6	Goal Setting	47
Chapter 7	SSB or CW?	51
Chapter 8	Propagation and Antennas	56
Chapter 9	Sending and Receiving QSLs	73
Chapter 10	Pileups	81
Chapter 11	DX Nets and Lists	89
Chapter 12	DXing in Contests	99
Chapter 13	DX Newsletters and Spotting Networks	103
Chapter 14	The DX Century Club (DXCC)	107
Chapter 15	Beyond DXCC	113

Preface

It is a winter evening, sometime in the late 1950s. A young boy sits before an old parlor radio, more than twice his age and nearly twice his size. He is tuning the shortwave broadcast bands. Voices and music from all over the world rattle through the 15-inch speaker; he can feel the vibrations in his knees, which are pressed against the speaker grill. The boy likes to draw maps and collect foreign stamps. He often has his nose stuck in a book about explorers, pirates or airplanes. Listening to broadcasts from across the sea adds another dimension to his interest in things far away.

One day, between foreign broadcast stations, he hears people talking to each other, mostly in English, but often using terms he does not understand. These people are not just *listening* to foreign countries, they are *communicating* with them!

In time, the idea germinates and after a few years of passive shortwave listening, the still-young boy becomes a Novice ham radio operator. His first receiver, a monster even older than the demised Philco, is replaced by a gleaming general-coverage receiver, with two tuning knobs and enormous semi-circular dials, a gift from his parents.

As quickly as possible, the boy drives his code speed up to 13 WPM and takes the General class license exam. Now it's time for a VFO (Novices were limited to 75 W input and crystal control in those ancient times). And it's time to get on 20 meters, where the DX is. (The receiver is somewhat lacking in stability on 15 meters.) Almost every night, until the boy goes off with his Uncle Sam, he tunes the bands, anticipating the next DX contact.

Now, almost thirty years later, the gleaming general-coverage receiver is retired, although the boy-at-heart still gives it a try now and then. In its place is a solid-state transceiver half its size. Although the location is in another call area, the equipment is modern, and the boy-at-heart is up much later than would have been allowed in his youth, the game is the same. He is working a pileup, anticipating his next DX contact. The years and miles melt away, for DXing truly transcends time and space.

DXing, as old as Amateur Radio itself, will always be a part of the hobby, no matter what new directions and technologies the future brings. Over the years, I have sampled many of the diverse operating modes Amateur Radio has to offer. DXing was my first love (in Amateur Radio, that is), and to it I return, again and again.

In the past, we used the Novice period of our Amateur Radio careers to get our techniques worked out. Then we were ready to reach out for some DX. Novice enhancement has changed all that. Today's new Novice or Technician is immediately thrown to the lions, so to speak, with little chance to learn the right moves.

This book began as a lengthy series of articles I wrote for new DXers of all license classes, to help them improve their skills and increase their pleasure in DXing. Mark Wilson, AA2Z, *QST*'s Managing Editor, suggested I rework the series into a book, instead. Within these pages, I hope to instill in you my appreciation for the sport of DXing and give you some hints to help you achieve your DXing goals.

DXing is a participatory sport, however. No book can fully illuminate its magic or explain its mysteries. And no book can take the place of actual on-the-air contact. If you wish to know the thrill of working DX, receiving QSLs from places you'd previously never heard of and making many lifelong friends around the world, you must get on the air and do it yourself. I hope though, that this little book will become your trusted guide and constant companion.

Many people contributed in some way to this book, but I'd like to single out a few for special thanks. Kirk Kleinschmidt, NTØZ, ARRL Editorial Supervisor, made countless valuable suggestions, and his editorial skills smoothed out many rough spots in the manuscript. Kirk's unceasing enthusiasm for this project made the final mechanical phases of its production a pleasure, not a chore.

Paul Shafer, KB1BE, made many valuable suggestions, which I was happy to incorporate. My thanks also to the other members of the Connecticut DX Association, who graciously filled out questionnaires and lent support in several ways.

Thanks to Chet Jones, NW1F, for the great cartoons.

Jim Kearman, KR1S
Newington, Connecticut

Chapter 1

What is DXing?

W orking DX—literally, communicating with distant stations —appeals to nearly every ham sooner or later. It starts innocently enough: You answer the CQ of a foreign station and marvel that your signal has traveled so far. Suddenly, you realize that the whole *world* is at your fingertips. You may continue to work domestic and foreign hams with equanimity, taking your DX casually when it comes along. Or you may find you're seeking out only foreign stations, particularly from countries you haven't worked yet.

THE GAME OF DXING

DXing is a game in which one station, with whom a contact is desired by other stations, tries to contact as many of them as possible. But while the DX station is willing to work anyone, working against the players at both ends are the vagaries of propagation and interference from hundreds or thousands of other stations trying to make contact at the same time.

Games were invented to simulate the primitive conditions of human survival: hunting and combat against Mother Nature, wild beasts and other men. Successful DXing requires tracking skills and propagation knowledge not unlike the talents of the big-game hunter. It doesn't hurt to have a "big gun" station, but the greatest weapon a DXer can have is operating skill, primarily the ability to listen. Any hunter (of animals or DX) knows that a big gun is of little value if you can't find the quarry, or your aim is poor.

There are dozens of books and courses to teach you how to become a radio amateur. The instruction manuals for your equipment show you how to operate it. But "how-to" books on DXing have always assumed a certain level of expertise. True, you can gain valuable experience by getting on the air and trying to work DX, learning from your mistakes. The trouble is, you mostly obtain only negative information: You know (or are told by others on the frequency!) that you are doing something wrong, but you don't know what's right! This book doesn't pretend to be the last word on DXing. If you are a newcomer to DXing, though, you will find here all the information you need to qualify for the coveted DXCC award.

DX VERSUS *RARE* DX

There is DX and there is *rare* DX. What's rare? Rare countries don't have active ham populations. They may be very near or very far, but activity is the determining factor, not distance. Of course, distant DX operators may be harder to work, but if they're active, sooner or later the determined DXer gets through. The religious enclave of Mt Athos would be easy to work from the anywhere in the United States *if* any active radio amateurs lived there! Japan or Australia on the other hand, although considerably farther away, can be easily worked from the US because both countries have many active hams. Likewise, working Desecheo Island, near Puerto Rico, should be like falling off a log from the US. But Desecheo is uninhabited and is only heard when some hardy souls decide to make the trip.

When you start DXing, you copy stations from places you never heard of, with exotic names you have to look up in the atlas. Your pulse quickens as you move in for the QSO. Then, in the next six months, you may work five more stations, each in those previously unknown (to you) countries. This is all well and good though, because you're gaining experience, especially in coping with DX anxiety! For example, I worked Henry, CE0FFD, on Easter Island, for the first time one autumn afternoon on 10 meters. I immediately sent my QSL card direct to Henry and congratulated myself on this DX coup. In the month it took for Henry's QSL to reach me, I heard him almost every day. He was often calling CQ *with no takers*!

DXPEDITIONS

Some "countries" that count for DXCC are uninhabited islands, like Desecheo, Bouvet, Peter I and Kingman Reef. Indeed, dozens of inhabited countries have no active hams. The harder-to-reach places are "activated" sometimes only once every ten years. When they are, it is a big event for DXers who haven't already worked them. The first DX-peditions were operated by amateurs who provided communications for explorers in the 1920s and '30s. Some DXpeditions today are by hams traveling on business or vacation. Others are exclusively Amateur Radio oriented and can cost more than $100,000 when all is said and done. Some fortunate amateurs go on multi-country DXpeditions almost every year. DXpedition expenses are paid by the operators, with assistance from various DX clubs, foundations and individual DXers.

WHAT'S THE ATTRACTION?

What causes otherwise sensible men and women to rise before dawn and stay up late into the night, straining their ears for weak signals from distant lands? For one thing, there's the challenge of competing, not just with other hams, but also against unpredictable propagation conditions. DXers are certainly drawn by the challenge, but most would tell you there's something more. For me, it's the adventure: never knowing what will appear at the next turn of the tuning knob. Will the Far East be coming through tonight on 15? What about tomorrow afternoon on 10? Each band has its own personality, which changes hour by hour. No two days are ever the same.

DXers live in the Garden of Ionospheric Delights. One day at sunset, signals from Japan are so strong on 40 CW you could mistake them for locals. The next day, there are no JAs to be heard, but a station in Jordan answers my CQ. Late that night, the polar path opens on 20 meters and I make my first SSB QSO with China. One late November afternoon, I simply tuned back and forth across 10 meters, engrossed in the experience of hearing stations from all six continents at the same time!

Later in this book, we'll discuss computer programs that graphically depict the areas of sunlight and darkness, calculate sunrise and sunset times and predict optimum times and frequencies for communications with other parts of the world. But nothing can replace the wisdom that comes from experience, or the excitement of being there as a band comes to life.

In this high-tech world, it's easy to forget that a naturally occurring phenomenon in the upper atmosphere is responsible for bringing these signals to us. Perhaps even more amazing in this diverse and often quarrelsome world is that our hobby has such universal appeal. Radio amateurs are truly citizens of the world. Regardless of racial and political differences, DXers everywhere identify with that common calling—to chase DX.

Through all the stages of the Cold War and its thaw, contacts with Soviet and Eastern European radio amateurs were commonplace. While our nonham neighbors watched the dismantling of the Berlin Wall on the evening news, DXers were sharing the ecstasy of East German hams. One ham in East Berlin, to whom I merely said, "Good luck with your new government," responded: "It is wonderful to be free." It was the next best thing to being there. With an average investment far less than a seat on the *Concorde*, DXers flit from country to country, continent to continent, at the speed of light.

DXers are perpetual students. How I envy the old-timers with their years of experience in reading band conditions, experimenting with antennas and learning how to get through when the going is rough. Although I often spend hours at the radio without making a contact, I always come away with some new knowledge.

Whatever attracts each of us to DXing, those who have been in the fire quickly gain a deep appreciation for their peers. DX clubs and conventions bring like-minded hams together and the in-person contact is as inspiring as the programs. Tomorrow we may be competing for a new country, but we're never strangers when we meet.

DXing is not all business, either: Late one night I answered the CQ of Marc, UQ2GUD, in Latvia. Marc gave me a signal report and his name and QTH, then told me I was his first United States QSO! After I gave him my exchange, he sent 73 and quickly signed off, probably to tell his family that he had gotten "across the pond." Marc must have been a new ham, as he wasn't listed in my *Callbook*. Memories of my first trans-Atlantic contact came to mind, undiminished by the passage of many years. I managed to hold him long enough to get his mailing address so I could send my QSL direct. I hope our brief QSO gave Marc a hint of the adventure that is DXing. By the time you read this book, Marc will have worked many US stations and will be looking for more exotic stuff to call, but the chances are good that he'll always remember his first DX QSO. So will you!

Chapter 2

Who are These DXers, Anyway?

W hat sort of person becomes a DXer? I was curious about that myself, so I passed out a questionnaire at my local DX club meeting. What I learned wasn't all that surprising: DXers are just like you and me! Most DXers are bitten by the DX bug early in their amateur careers. They seem to stay with it, although they may also have other Amateur Radio interests. SSB and CW are the favorite modes of course, but each mode is equally popular.

DXers are wallpaper chasers, with Worked All Continents (WAC) and DXCC being the most popular awards. Most DXers do operate in DX contests, but their emphasis is more on working new countries than on running up a score.

Most DXers I asked spend from two to five hours a week chasing DX. Many devote more than 10 hours a week to the sport. When asked what they liked most about DXing, their answers varied, but the constant theme was: "The challenge, the competition and the thrill of the chase."

While I was writing this chapter, I experienced one of those mornings that keeps my interest in DXing at a high pitch. It was just after sunrise, on a Friday morning in mid May. A DXpedition to Conway Reef, in the South Pacific, was due to be on the air and I was looking for it on 20-meter CW. Conway Reef had been on before, but it wasn't in my log. Sure enough, I found the crew on 14023 kHz, listening above their transmitting frequency. As I tuned through the pileup, I heard HS0AC, in Thailand, at about 14027 kHz. Another country I needed! The Conway Reef operation was keeping most of the DXers occupied, so I had a clear shot at HS0AC. One call, and a new country was in my log. Then, back down to the pileup. A few minutes later, I bagged Conway Reef. A further look around the CW band showed nothing else I needed, although South Pacific stations were numerous and loud. So I slipped up to the SSB part of the band, only to find V85GA, in Brunei, *another* country I needed! It took me a little longer to break that pileup, but I soon had Brunei in the bag.

Some hams would shrug and say, "So what? Why get excited about three 10-second contacts?" DXers need no explanation or excuse. There's something magical about turning on the radio and hearing a new one, not to mention *three* new ones in a row. But the magic doesn't work on every ham.

I guess DXers are more susceptible to it than non DXers. What effect does that DX magic have on you?

If you've listened to the pileup on a DX station, you've noticed that some stations seem to take "getting through" more seriously than others. These "serious" operators always seem to be a little stronger and more persistent—sometimes even a little pushy! Maybe you don't take it so seriously now, but maybe you will later.

You may think you can't compete against stronger signals and strong wills. Don't believe that for even a second. DXing is an acquired taste. Successful DXers adapt to the sport by developing "can't lose" attitudes, learning the necessary skills and building better stations. The station you can buy, but the attitude and skills come only from experience. This book is mostly about skills, but let's examine the attitude first.

THE DXER'S ATTITUDE

Amateur Radio began with radio "hackers," unlicensed wireless experimenters. The hobby was organized as a noncommercial means of relaying messages across the country. In keeping with this concept, our national organization was named the American Radio Relay League. Before long, amateurs found they could work coast-to-coast, without relays. In the early '20s, the oceans were spanned and DXing was born. At this point, message content became less important than the fact that messages had been exchanged. QSL cards became the standard method for confirming a contact. The mark of the DXer was the number of countries confirmed. In 1937, the ARRL announced the DX Century Club, open to any licensed radio amateur who could confirm contacts with at least 100 countries.

Then, as now, certain operators, whether message (traffic) handlers or DXers, eschewed ragchewing. Ragchewers *are* exchanging informal traffic and may occasionally work foreign stations. DXers exchange messages too, but once again, the content is less relevant than the fact that an *exchange* is made. A DXer seeks to *communicate* with other amateurs in as many different countries as possible, period.

Some people think DXing is shallow, because the contents of the communication are usually trivial. DXing is a sport, a sort of radio gymnastics. I asked a friend what he liked most about DXing. His answer was simple, but full of meaning: "Just knowing I can!" To DXers, the medium is the message.

Like any sport, DXing has rules, written and understood. It has strategies and tactics, wins and losses, superstars and casual players. DXing has even suffered a few scandals. In your career as a DXer you will encounter thousands of other hams. The ones you notice the most are often not the most successful. They may in fact be the least successful. While you're looking for models, carefully consider each operating tactic and trait before you adopt it. You want to learn from the violinists, not the fiddle players.

IS THERE AN AVERAGE DXER?

About the only way to describe the average DXer is in terms of that "can't lose" attitude I spoke of earlier. Beyond that, DXers come in many varieties. Most of us started out running about 100 W to wire or vertical antennas. A three-element triband beam for 20, 15 and 10 meters is usually next on the agenda. Many DXers are satisfied with this setup; indeed, given the right conditions, you can work every country that shows up on these three bands. Every new DXer wants to achieve DXCC. Some hams lose interest once they have the certificate. Others see having 100 countries confirmed as just one stop on the way to the DXCC Honor Roll.

Becoming a DXer means making a commitment to achieving goals. For most of us, the commitment is mainly one of time. We like to talk to our friends, too. But when we are DXing, we are DXing! What distinguishes a DXer from a casual operator on the same band? Given limited operating time, the DXer spends it looking for new countries, not ragchewing. That competitive, goal-oriented personality, always seeking challenges, is the common trait of DXers.

Unlike many forms of competition, DXing is a sport in which you can participate from home. You decide how much time and money to invest. You set your own goals and determine your own pace. It took me more than 27 years of on-again, off-again operating to confirm 100 countries. The bug bit hard the second time though, and the next 100 fell in six months! Yet, as I started this book, I was reminded of a DXer who recently became a member of the Honor Roll (see Chapter 15) at age 27. He was an infant when I became a ham, but he has worked more than 100 more countries than me! Right now, I'm glad I'm not him, because I have more than 100 countries left to work and many more exciting sunrises to anticipate.

Chapter 3

What Do I Need to Be a DXer?

Exotic setups are much more photogenic than a barefoot transceiver in the basement, so they get better coverage in the magazines. Believe it or not, even if you don't yet own a radio, you already have the most important ingredient of an effective station: You, the operator, with an interest in the subject and a willingness to learn. If you maintain this attitude, I guarantee you will be successful, even if you don't have a cover-story station!

Let's look at an "average" DXer's station. Where is it? Oh, there on the table. Gosh, no big racks full of high-power tubes, but quite a bit of "wallpaper"—QSLs and awards. A nice transceiver, although not the latest model. It can transmit and receive on separate frequencies, though, and that's important. There's the rotator control box for the triband beam outside and an antenna tuner for the 80-meter dipole. It does double duty as a 40-meter antenna as well. There's a dummy load, too, for testing without putting a signal on the air.

The ARRL logbook is easy to read, thanks to the light from a lamp on the left side of the table. A microphone and a shiny keyer paddle grace the desk. A shelf off to the side holds the *Callbooks*, the *DXCC Countries List* and a world atlas. The 24-hour digital clock is placed right above the transceiver so the DXers (there are three) in this family don't have to crane their necks to see the time.

The family sports one Advanced-class licensee, one Novice and one Technician. They've agreed to get a linear amplifier when all three have upgraded at least to General class. As a matter of fact, an electrician is scheduled to install a special 220-V line to the shack for just that purpose.

It's a simple station, but it has accounted for more than 200 countries among the three operators. Unfortunately, many hams think that successful DXing requires gigantic antenna systems, the latest equipment and a mountaintop QTH.

Most DXers have simple stations, without frills and gadgets. Through experience they have learned how much equipment is necessary to be successful and that simple stations are easier to operate. For equipment, you *need* a transceiver (or a transmitter and a receiver), an antenna, a keyer and paddle, headphones, a microphone, a 24-hour digital clock and a logbook. If your antenna is fed with twin lead, you'll need a Transmatch. Anything else is a luxury.

TRANSCEIVERS VERSUS "SEPARATES?"

If you are buying a new rig, you don't have much choice here; very few separate transmitter/receiver pairs are still made. If you're buying used equipment however, there are good buys to be had in second-hand transmitters and receivers. Being able to "transceive," that is, adjust the operating frequency of both boxes with one tuning knob, is very useful, so be sure to purchase compatible units.

Until recently, having a separate transmitter and receiver was almost a necessity because of the limitations of most transceivers. Today's transceivers have overcome these drawbacks, however, and dominate the market. DXers often transmit on a frequency from 2 kHz to 60 kHz or more above or below their receive frequency. Most older transceivers can't accomplish this feat, which explains the popularity of "separates."

SPLITTING UP IS HARD TO DO (WITHOUT)

If there is one quality that the DXer's station must have, it is the ability to "split" the transmit and receive frequencies. If you are looking at used transceivers, this is the first test of their suitability. Note that the RIT (receiver incremental tuning) control is *not* up to the task. Most RIT controls can shift the receiver frequency only a few kilohertz. To accomplish split-frequency operation, a transceiver must have two tuning controls. They usually function one at a time and a switch allows you to select between them. Some older transceivers can be used with a remote VFO. They can be operated split. If you buy a used transceiver with a remote VFO, all is well and good. Be aware that the chances of turning up only a remote VFO are slim. If the rig doesn't come with one, it's probably not for you.

FREQUENCY COVERAGE

Equipment made before 1979 is unlikely to allow operation on the so-called "WARC bands," 30, 17 and 12 meters. Even some equipment built since then does not offer these bands. Activity on these bands is growing steadily and they offer many alternatives as propagation conditions change. If you're buying a rig, you should seriously consider one that covers the WARC bands. The 160-meter band may also be excluded from earlier rigs; but, if the rig covers the WARC bands, it probably covers 160, too.

POWER OUTPUT

Most transmitters or transceivers run from 80 to 150 W output. Less than 80 W is somewhat limiting, more than 150 W is unnecessary. Rigs in this power-output range produce a reasonable signal "barefoot," and can adequately drive almost any linear amplifier.

TUBE, OR NOT TUBE?

All currently produced transceivers are completely solid state. Some recent equipment is "hybrid"; the receiver may be all solid state, while the transmitter uses both vacuum tubes and solid-state components. There is nothing inherently wrong with hybrid equipment, except that vacuum tubes are getting pretty expensive and somewhat hard to find. As a general rule, avoid equipment that uses only tubes.

THE RECEIVER

Generating a reasonable 100-W signal is relatively easy; building a good receiver is not. It is primarily the quality of the receiver that separates the good rigs from the bad. The qualities of a good receiver are:
- Stability
- Selectivity
- Immunity from strong signals on nearby frequencies

The stability of most solid-state receivers is adequate, but the other two factors are not guaranteed. The receiver should at least have provisions for a narrow CW filter of 500- or 250-Hz bandwidth. Immunity from strong, nearby signals is greatly enhanced if the selectivity can be improved. Some receivers can be equipped with two internal filters. This option is worthwhile, as it will help you dig a DX station out of the noise when propagation is poor. Also, not everyone runs a clean signal; good selectivity helps you ignore a broad, raspy signal a few kilohertz up the band.

Immunity from blocking, the decrease in sensitivity caused by a strong signal adjacent to the one you're trying to copy, is desirable. Although improved internal selectivity (external audio filters won't help) goes a long way in this regard, the receiver must be properly designed from the start to offer good blocking immunity.

How do you know what to buy? *QST* product reviews are an excellent source of information. All new transceivers reviewed in *QST* are put through a standardized test regimen, allowing reliable performance comparisons. Perhaps a local ham or your library has back issues you can read, or you can write to the ARRL Technical Information Service for assistance. The ARRL will *not* recommend one rig over another, but does provide technical information available on the equipment in which you are interested.

If you have a chance to operate equipment before you buy, so much the better. Bear in mind, though, you won't really begin to appreciate a radio's attributes until you've used it for a while. One last observation: With new ham equipment, you pretty much get what you pay for.

ANTENNAS

No facet of Amateur Radio has been responsible for more books and articles than antennas. In fact, half of Chapter 8 is dedicated to a more in-depth discussion of the different types of antennas. For now, let's keep it simple. While every DXer wants directional beam antennas, you can readily work more than 100 countries with simple wire and vertical antennas. Few DXers start out with large rotary beams on tall towers. Although no one who started out with only wire antennas and moved on to beams is likely to want to go back to wires again, they would all agree that the early lessons learned with simple antennas continue to pay dividends today. Your antenna installation will be limited by several factors, not all of them within your control. Aside from the cost of putting up a tower and one or more beams, not everyone lives in a place where such an installation is physically possible or allowed.

In fact, a major advantage of nondirectional antennas for beginning DXers is that they *are* nondirectional. It takes time to learn where to point a beam at various times of the day on different bands and there may be other paths unexpectedly open at the same time. Not having to fool with a rotator makes searching the bands much easier. If a band is open, chances are you'll find a country you need that you can work fairly easily with a simple antenna.

Experimenting with antennas you build yourself is a fascinating and educating hobby in itself. I always try to have two antennas in place for each band, even if one of them is only a dipole, so I can switch between them and compare their performance. Wire antennas are a blessing for the experimenter, as they are inexpensive and easy to put up and conceal.

Regardless of what antenna type you decide to use, place the antenna as high as safely possible. Even a simple dipole is a surprisingly good performer when it's a half wavelength or more off the ground and away from electrical wires and other conducting objects. Even if you're limited to indoor antennas, a dipole strung up in the attic or crawl space will work plenty of DX.

Vertical antennas are excellent DX performers and are easy to make. Using a simple wire vertical with four radials, I worked 46 countries in five days while on vacation in Florida. When I lived in a New York City apartment house, I managed to load up the fire escape on 160, 80, and 40 meters. My QSL collection includes cards from Australia and New

Zealand for contacts made from that antenna. The lesson here: Don't let the lack of a big antenna system deter you from trying your hand at DXing.

KEYS AND KEYERS

CW operation should be done with an electronic keyer and paddle. Even if you have a keyboard, you should be proficient with the paddle. Keyboards sometimes break, paddles rarely do. Yes, there are straight keys and semi-automatic "bugs," but the cleanest hand-sent CW is done with a keyer. You need absolute accuracy when you are calling a DX station. You may only get your call sign through once; if the DX station copies what you sent, but what you sent wasn't really your call, you are going to be one unhappy DXer.

There are two types of electronic keyers: iambic and noniambic. Iambic paddles have two lever arms; a noniambic paddle has only one. When you squeeze the iambic paddle (connected to an iambic keyer), a series of alternating dits and dahs is sent. Iambic keying makes most letters easier to send. Less fatigue means fewer mistakes. Learn to send code with an iambic paddle and key. Making the transition from noniambic to iambic can be a bit tricky, but it's hardly impossible.

Many modern transceivers have built-in keyers. This makes for a compact station. The advantage of an external keyer, however, is ready access to all the controls, such as the "weighting" control, which you can to use to make the dits a little longer (for punching through noise). Built-in keyers usually allow access only to the speed control.

Memory Keyers

If you decide to buy a keyer, a memory keyer is a good investment. A memory keyer allows you to store long or short strings of characters, such as "599," "599 NY," or even a complete transmission of RST, QTH and name. There will be times when you will be repeatedly sending your call sign for extended periods of time, trying to crack a pileup. Using a memory keyer ensures that your call is always sent correctly. When the big moment comes and you get through, you just punch another button to send your exchange, while you collapse from the excitement! Memory keyers come in many varieties, but all work pretty much the same way. Some have built-in computers with which you can have QSOs. This feature is handy for training and when the bands are really dead.

HEADPHONES

Headphones are not a luxury to a DXer, they are an important tool. Even if your shack is completely soundproof, no loudspeaker is as sensitive as even the least-expensive headphones. DXing often requires you to dig for a signal, and good headphones are an enormous help. Most hams use stereo headphones and most transceivers are wired so you can plug them right into the headphone jack without an adapter. Adapters are also available to convert the stereo plug to mono, or you can change the plug. Stay away from inexpensive "walkman type" stereo headphones and stick with audiophile-quality headphones. You'll never regret the expense. When you have to, you can turn up the audio gain to drag out a weak signal without worrying about the things disintegrating on your head. Here again, you get what you pay for.

MICROPHONES

Most of today's transceivers are supplied with hand-held microphones. Hand-held mikes are fine for mobile operation, but you need something better at home. Some exotic microphones are available with built-in equalizers, but unless you have an unusual voice, an equalizer is probably not necessary—if you have a good mike to begin with. The audio circuits of even the best amateur equipment, however, do not seem to accurately reproduce many female voices. This is one area where some equalization is helpful. Yet again, you get what you pay for. If you have a hand-held mike, you can always use it until you decide what you want to buy. Meanwhile, if you work someone whose audio sounds really impressive, ask what mike he is using.

Consider mounting the microphone on a boom, like those used in broadcast studios. This arrangement gives you more space on the table. When you're not using it, you can just swing it out of the way.

Another possibility is a headset, a combination headphone and microphone. If you wear a headset, the mike follows you wherever you go. Contesters like them because they allow relative freedom of movement—an important consideration when you operate for several hours without stopping.

24-HOUR CLOCK

All DXers and DX stations use 24-hour Coordinated Universal Time (UTC; see the sidebar). So, you need a 24-hour clock. Some attractive analog (you remember, the ones with hands) clocks are available. If you receive one as a gift, display it prominently in your shack, but use a *24-hour* digital clock for logging. Don't try to use a 12-hour clock and make the conversions in your head. A mistake here can cost you a QSL card. DX stations make so many contacts that neither they nor their QSL managers have time to search through the logs looking for your contact.

I am so concerned about keeping accurate time that I use a battery-

TIME KEEPING

If you start on the East Coast of the US and travel west, you seem to move back in time. When it's 6 AM on the East Coast, it's 3 AM on the West Coast, 4 AM in the Rocky Mountains, and 5 AM in the Midwest.

Time zones fall more or less on "meridians" of longitude, those imaginary north-south lines we see on maps and globes. Longitude is measured in degrees east and west of 0° longitude, which happens to run through an observatory in Greenwich, England.

There are 360° in a circle and there are 360° of longitude around the earth. 180° east and 180° west of the Greenwich meridian is the International Date Line. Each day has 24 hours and the earth rotates once a day, so each 15 degrees of longitude equals one hour of time (360/24 = 15). Knowing this, you can approximate the time at any point on the globe for which you know the longitude. (Not all countries or areas adhere to this "standard," however.)

For many years, DXers set their clocks to Greenwich Mean Time, or GMT. You still see QSL cards printed with GMT in the time block. Technology caught up with the Greenwich clock, however, and more accurate devices are used to measure the passage of time. Time measured by one of these standards is called Coordinated Universal Time, or UTC. For our purposes, the mean time in Greenwich is just fine. There is no such thing as Greenwich Daylight Savings Time, although Great Britain does observe Savings Time in the summer.

Why use UTC? It's the internationally recognized standard time. Every DXer knows how many hours difference there is between his local time and UTC. That way, when you work BY9GA in China, the times in both logs are the same (give or take a minute or so). There really is no other time to use. Don't try to keep your log in local time and convert the times when you fill out QSL cards. Sooner or later, you'll make an error and the DX station's log for the time you gave will show nothing that resembles your call.

There's more. If the Greenwich meridian is four or more hours ahead of any time zone in the United States, it may be tomorrow there when it's still today here. Get it? During Central Standard Time (CST) in the United States, when it's one minute after midnight in Greenwich, it's only 6:01 PM CST. You have to keep track of the UTC date in your log, as well as the time. Just remember to advance the date when your clock shows 0000 UTC.

Another part of time-keeping that confuses some new DXers is the use of 24-hour time. It really isn't so hard once you think about it. There are 24 hours in a day. For some reason though, we think of a day as having two 12-hour pieces. So at noon we start counting the hours all over again. When we say "eleven o'clock," we either specify "AM" or "PM," or assume the person we're talking to understands which half of the day we mean.

The 24-hour system leaves no doubt. There is no AM or PM in 24-hour time. Instead of starting over at 1 PM, we say "13 hours." Note that the colon (:) is usually not used in the 24-hour system. Five-thirty in the afternoon is 1730 hours (12 + 5 = 17 hours, or 1700; adding the thirty minutes gives 1730).

Fortunately, modern DXers have access to digital, 24-hour clocks. Every shack should have one.

North American hams are also fortunate in having the National Institute of Standards and Technology radio stations to listen to. No matter where you live, you should have good propagation on at least one frequency used by WWV or WWVH. Their frequencies are 2.5, 5, 10, 15, and 20 MHz, (WWV only), *exactly*, so they make good references for checking equipment frequency calibration, too. Time in UTC is given every minute on both stations. They both transmit interesting propagation information every hour, which is discussed in Chapter 6.

Most modern amateur-band receivers include at least one WWV frequency in their coverage. If you have a transceiver incorporating a general-coverage receiver, you can receive them all. Or, you can buy a combination WWV/National Weather Service receiver in most consumer-electronics stores.

operated clock. This clock is totally immune to power failures. If the battery goes dead, so does the display. My clock is the least-expensive accessory in your shack, but it gives me the most peace of mind! If you buy an ac-operated clock with battery backup, make sure of two things: The display should flash whenever power is interrupted, and it should have a visible indicator to tell you that the backup battery is still fresh. By the way, another benefit of a battery-only clock is that you can unplug *everything* in your shack when you're not on the air (for lightning protection), without having to reset the clock each time you want to operate.

STATION LAYOUT

Not only are most DXers' stations simple, they are arranged for maximum efficiency. All frequently adjusted controls are within easy reach, as are *Callbooks*, an atlas and the *DXCC Countries List*. Devices that are infrequently used may be positioned farther away. Lighting should be soft, but bright enough to prevent straining to see the log or station controls. Your chair should be comfortable, but not so comfortable that you fall asleep. All cables and wires should be positioned so that people can move around in your shack without tripping or being strangled.

CALL DIRECTORIES

The *Radio Amateur's Callbook* is published annually (in November) in two volumes. One volume lists all licensed radio amateurs in North America; the other volume covers the rest of the world. Mailing addresses (as provided by the licensing authorities in each country) are given for almost every radio amateur listed. The exceptions are some republics in the Soviet Union, for which only the licensees' names are given. You need the current editions of both volumes. A supplement is published in the summer which updates both volumes.

THE STATION LOG

Although it's positioned at the end of this chapter, keeping an accurate station log is so important that the next chapter is dedicated entirely to that subject. If you're preparing a budget or a shopping list, don't forget the ARRL logbook.

Chapter 4

Getting Organized

I heard some talk on one of the DX nets about a Japanese DXpedition to Minami Torishima, a country I need. They even mentioned the operating frequencies to be used. I think my best bet would be on 10 meters, which opens to the northern Pacific area in the evenings at my location. Let's see, they're going in August. I remember working a slew of stations in Japan on 10 meters last August. Let's have a look at that log, which is right here on the shelf. Oh, yes, I had my best luck about 7 PM Eastern Daylight Time, or 2300 UTC. Okay, now I know when my best chance will be, and I won't even have to leave work early!

Here's 5Z4BI handing out reports on 10 meters. I never seem to catch him on 10, although I worked him on 15 meters last week. Let's see…here it is, in the log at 1900 UTC. I didn't send a card last week because I was hoping to work him on 10 meters soon. Good, I got him. Last week he told me his QSL manager was W4FRU. Guess that hasn't changed in a week. Now for a look at the ARRL *DXCC Countries List*. Just as I thought, I haven't confirmed Kenya on either band, so I'll send two cards.

DATE	FREQ.	MODE	POWER	TIME	STATION WORKED	REPORT SENT	REPORT REC'D	TIME OFF	QTH	COMMENTS NAME	QSL VIA	QSL S	QSL R
9/2	28	SSB	100	1405	OH1AF	59-1	58			SCAND. CONTEST		✓	
				1407	OHØA1	59-2						✓	
				1410	SMØAGD	59	59			ERIK	Buro	✓	
				1511	FT5XA	59	51		KERGUELEN ISL!		F61TD	²/₃	⁹/₁₄
9/3	21	CW	100	1703	ISØMH	579	579		SARDINIA	GAB		✓	
				1715	G13OLJ	579	579		BANGOR	JOHN		✓	
				1720	HB9AAK	589	579			RUDY			
				1733	HKØBEX	599	599				WB9NUC	⁹/₅	
	28	SSB		1909	HZ1AB	55	54			TERRY	K8PYD	⁹/₅	
				1915	WB16HL					MARK			

Although station logbooks are no longer required by the FCC, they're a necessity for DXers. In additon to tracking QSL submissions, your station log is a storehouse of DX and personal information that you'll refer to time after time.

Glossary of Terms

Prefix Allocation Table—A table that lists the Amateur Radio call sign prefixes assigned to each country by the International Telecommunication Union. This is useful for determining the location of stations that have unusual call signs.

WAS—Worked All States award. This award, sponsored by the ARRL, is awarded to amateurs who confirm contact with stations in all 50 US states.

Five-Band DXCC—5BDXCC is awarded to amateurs who confirm contact with stations in at least 100 DXCC countries on each of five HF amateur bands: 80, 40, 20, 15 and 10 meters.

Endorsement—Continuing operating achievements beyond the "basic" DXCC award are recognized by various endorsements. For example, if your basic DXCC award shows you confirmed 106 DXCC countries, you can add endorsement stickers to the basic award when you reach 125, 150 and 200 countries, and so on.

I want to remember that I sent the cards direct to W4FRU, so I'll write the date in the "SENT" column. If I had sent them to 5Z4BI via the bureau, I'd just put a check mark in that spot. Now the paperwork is finished, let's try for another new one before dinner.

Aha, here's a big signal from South Africa, another country I need on 10 meters. I worked him on 20 meters a while back and sent a card direct, along with two IRCs. That was last winter. Check the log...yes, here's the info he gave me—name, address, and so on. I never did receive a card in return. But listen to that pileup. Sure hope those folks get a QSL for their trouble. I think I'll wait for a tourist to go down there and operate. For now, I'll keep tuning.

Here's a nice pileup. It's a 9Q5, in Zaire. I know I have it confirmed, but I better check the *DXCC Countries List*. Yes, I do, on 10 and 15 meters. That's good. I sure don't fancy trying to navigate that pileup. Keep tuning. Wait—here's a weak CQ. The voice sounds American, but there are plenty of Americans in Africa. Good, it's 3DAØXV. Gosh, I just worked him on 20 meters a few nights ago. Flip back a couple pages...yep, it's Roman. He lives in South Africa and only gets to Swaziland occasionally. I need him on this band! It'll be nice to call him by name and with those pileups down the band I'll have him all to myself! Glad I didn't waste time with them; I just got the call for dinner.

THOSE FAR-OUT PREFIXES

Ah, a DX contest weekend. My wife is visiting her sister and I have plenty of coffee on hand. The contest has started, so let's see what's on. Wow, here's a new one for sure, 5J6CQ. Where the heck is that? Must be someplace rare, judging by the pileup. Someone on his frequency is asking, "What's his QTH?" He's not in the *DXCC Countries List*, so I'll look in the Prefix Table in back (it's also in the ARRL logbook). Ah, the 5JJ block is assigned to Colombia, so this is really an HK6, which I have confirmed on all bands. Because I'm not a prefix collector, I'll come back for the multiplier when the pileup thins out.

If you'll take a look at the prefix allocation table, you'll see that most countries are allocated more than one block of prefixes. The US, for example, can use AAA-ALZ, KAA-KZZ, NAA-NZZ, WAA-WZZ and so on. Amateur call signs in the US are issued from all of these blocks, although so far we only have one- and two-letter prefixes. The FCC no longer issues special prefixes or call signs, but other countries do. Having a unique prefix helps you stand out in a contest and attracts calls from prefix hunters who might not otherwise want a QSO. For example, France occasionally issues calls from the FV block to special-events stations. Knowing the rarity of such French-colony prefixes as FK, FS, or FT, your ears really perk up when you hear an FV!

Unfortunately, there is no way of knowing in advance which French prefixes are in France and which are colonies or territories. Our country offers the same dilemma. You can't tell from the Prefix Allocation Table that KH2 is Guam, but KD2 is only New York or New Jersey. However, in the case of Colombia, there are fewer off-shore entities to worry about. Colombia issues HK0-prefix calls to San Andres and Malpelo Islands. So, if you should hear a 5J0 prefix, you could probably assume the station was on one of those islands.

It's worthwhile to learn the standard prefixes listed in the *DXCC Countries List*, although they number more than 300. Many of them you hear almost every day, such as DL, F, G, HA, I, JA and the various K/W prefixes.

Some of the prefixes, though, look a little strange until you hear them on the air. For example, Europa Island is listed as FR/E in the *DXCC Countries List* and Juan de Nove is listed as FR/J. FR is the prefix for Reunion Island. Typical Reunion calls are FR5AI or FR5DD. A station licensed to operate from Europa Island would be issued a call like FR5EA; for Juan de Nova Island, the call might be FR5JA. The E or J after the number indicates Europa or Juan de Nova, respectively. When FR5AI (a Reunion licensee) goes to Europa, he signs FR5AI/E.

As long as countries issue call signs from their alloction blocks, they don't have to stick to logical prefix assignments. And sometimes they don't. The DX newsletters try to keep abreast of who's signing what, where. A good rule of thumb is, if you think you need it, work it, or "Work First, Worry Later" (WFWL).

KEEPING A LOG

Keeping an accurate, orderly log is absolutely essential for even the occasional DXer. Chapter 3 discusses the importance of using the UTC time and date. Every entry in your log should be legible and accurate, so you can confidently fill out your QSL card. If a station gives a QSL route, either a mailing address or the call of his QSL manager, make sure you enter that information completely. Operating frequency and mode are also important. Although regulations don't require you to log the exact operating frequency, it's a good idea. Many DX stations seem to prefer certain frequencies. You may wish to look for the station again to set up a schedule for another band. A friend may need that country and you'll be able to indicate exactly where you worked it.

The last two columns on the ARRL logbook are where you note whether you sent and received a QSL. If I send the card through the bureau, I simply place a check mark in the S (sent) column. But if I send the card through the mail, I enter the date in that column. That way I know the route I used. When I receive a card, I enter the date in the R (received) column. If I should work this station for a new country on another band, I have some idea of how long it took to get the last card (or if I got one at all!).

The DXCC Countries List

You're tuning across 15 meters and you hear 3A2LC working a pileup. You know you've worked 3A (Monaco) before, but was it on 10 or 15, phone or CW? Will you have to look back through your logs and QSLs to find out? Not if you keep a copy of the *DXCC Countries List* handy! Properly filled out, the *List* can tell you at a glance which countries you have worked and confirmed on each band and mode, including RTTY and satellite QSOs. It is the nature of a ham to try to improve his or her equipment and accessories, and the *DXCC Countries List*, as useful as it is, is a good candidate for modification. I use different-color felt-tip underliner pens to mark the vertical columns in my *Countries List*. I can quickly scan down the list to see if I need a country on a particular band (I'm planning ahead for Five-Band DXCC). On the left side of each page are three columns, labeled Mixed, Phone and CW. Go through your log and mark an X for each country you have worked, in the appropriate mode column. (Mixed applies to CW, phone and RTTY, but not satellite.) Be sure to put an X in the appropriate band column, too. By the way, you can label the last, blank, column for 30 meters, 6 meters or QRP if you work those bands or modes.

As you receive QSL cards, sort them in exactly the same order as the *Countries List.* Each time you confirm a country, color in the appropriate boxes on the *List* with a contrasting ink (I use red). When

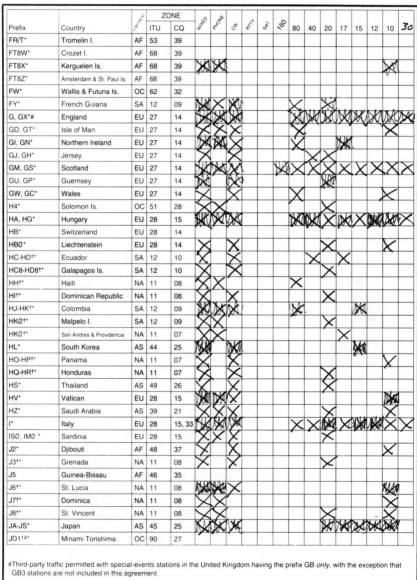

Prefix	Country		ITU	CQ	MIXED	PHONE	CW	RTTY	SAT	160	80	40	20	17	15	12	10	30
FR/T*	Tromelin I.	AF	53	39														
FT8W*	Crozet I.	AF	68	39														
FT8X*	Kerguelen Is.	AF	68	39														
FT8Z*	Amsterdam & St. Paul Is.	AF	68	39														
FW*	Wallis & Futuna Is.	OC	62	32														
FY*	French Guiana	SA	12	09														
G, GX*#	England	EU	27	14														
GD, GT*	Isle of Man	EU	27	14														
GI, GN*	Northern Ireland	EU	27	14														
GJ, GH*	Jersey	EU	27	14														
GM, GS*	Scotland	EU	27	14														
GU, GP*	Guernsey	EU	27	14														
GW, GC*	Wales	EU	27	14														
H4*	Solomon Is.	OC	51	28														
HA, HG*	Hungary	EU	28	15														
HB*	Switzerland	EU	28	14														
HB0*	Liechtenstein	EU	28	14														
HC-HD†*	Ecuador	SA	12	10														
HC8-HD8†*	Galapagos Is.	SA	12	10														
HH†*	Haiti	NA	11	08														
HI†*	Dominican Republic	NA	11	08														
HJ-HK†*	Colombia	SA	12	09														
HK0†*	Malpelo I.	SA	12	09														
HK0†*	San Andres & Providencia	NA	11	07														
HL*	South Korea	AS	44	25														
HO-HP†*	Panama	NA	11	07														
HQ-HR†*	Honduras	NA	11	07														
HS*	Thailand	AS	49	26														
HV*	Vatican	EU	28	15														
HZ*	Saudi Arabia	AS	39	21														
I*	Italy	EU	28	15, 33														
IS0, IM0 *	Sardinia	EU	28	15														
J2*	Djibouti	AF	48	37														
J3†*	Grenada	NA	11	08														
J5	Guinea-Bissau	AF	46	35														
J6†*	St. Lucia	NA	11	08														
J7†*	Dominica	NA	11	08														
J8†*	St. Vincent	NA	11	08														
JA-JS*	Japan	AS	45	25														
JD1¹⁴*	Minami Torishima	OC	90	27														

#Third-party traffic permitted with special-events stations in the United Kingdom having the prefix GB *only*, with the exception that GB3 stations are not included in this agreement.

A page from *The ARRL DXCC Countries List.*

you apply for DXCC and the card has been accepted for credit, fill the box in black. Now you can tell at a glance what countries you have worked and confirmed on each band and mode and which ones you've already turned in for credit.

Shoe boxes are a traditional repository for QSL cards, but I prefer a card-file drawer. The 4 × 6-inch size will hold all standard-size domestic and foreign QSLs. Index dividers help you locate the right place quickly and help prevent misfiling. The drawer shown below will hold about 1500 cards; it should be many years before you need a second one!

QSL card binders are available from *QST* advertisers. These binders are designed to hold cards for DXCC, WAS and other awards. If you like to show off your cards (and who doesn't?), a binder is probably more "user friendly" than a file drawer.

Although you're planning ahead for Five-Band DXCC, for now you're only going to call stations in those countries that you have never worked, as indicated on your *Countries List*, unless you do not have a QSL card from that country. Then you are wise to work the country again. (I keep a computer-sorted printout of all the stations I have worked, showing the bands and modes, to avoid working the same station twice on the same band.) Assuming your operating time is limited, you want to spend it looking for new countries, not working the same ones over

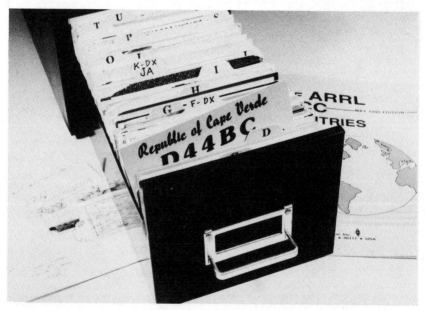

A 5- × 7-inch card file is a handy way to organize your QSL card collection.

and over, so use discretion.

Although accurate record keeping requires a little more time, as you work and confirm more and more countries on various bands you'll always know exactly which countries you have or need on every band and mode you operate.

```
                RUSSIAN PREFIXES WORKED BUT NOT CONFIRMED

                LIST PREPARED: December 6, 1989


        CALL              BAND         DATE              INFO

    RF2V/UB5IFN            7         10/21/89
    RF6FO                 14          8/6/89
    RI8AI                 14          9/22/89
    RI8BZZ                14          9/3/89
    RM8MA                 14         10/3/89
    RO40A                 28         10/15/89
    RO40A                  7         11/4/89
    RT6/UJ8W              14          8/9/89        HAVE ROUTE
    UA3EAC/RF5Q           14
    UA3LAR/RF9Q           14
    UA3QAG/RF3Q           14
    UB4IYU/UG1            14
    UB4JDM/RG             14
    UB5IRZ/UG8G           14          9/20/89
    UF6AW                 21          9/11/89
    UF6DZ                 14         11/16/89
    UF6FDR                 7         11/2/89
    UF6QAC                14          8/9/89        HAVE DIRECT ADR
    UG/UV3ZZ              14         10/3/89        VIA UA9AB
    UH8AAD                14         10/2/89
    UH8ED                 14         11/7/89
    UI8AA                 14         11/11/89
    UI8IT/UI1CK           21         10/15/89
    UM8AV                 14         11/8/89
    UM8MM                 14         11/8/89
    UO40R                 28
    UO5AP                 14          9/9/89
    UO50AK               14.2        11/12/89
    UO50AL                21
    UO50B                 14          9/9/89
    UO50JO                14          8/9/89
    UO50KS                14         11/1/89
    UO50N                  7
    UO5WT                 14          9/9/89
```

After your QSL card collection grows, keeping track of your cards is often easier with a computer data base. That way, it's easier to track cards for multiple awards, because the computer can sort the same list of QSL cards in many different ways. This printout shows my list of Russian prefixes worked, but not confirmed.

COMPUTERIZED RECORD-KEEPING

There are several computer programs available that you can use for logging contacts and keeping track of QSLs sent and received. Some programs even tell you when you've qualified to apply for DXCC or an endorsement, and can prepare the DXCC application forms for you. If you have access to a personal computer, you may wish to consider automating your records. Remember to keep a backup disk and a printed copy of your records in case of computer problems.

Chapter 5

Your First DX Contact

A re you ready to work some DX? Let's go! It'll be easier on SSB, so let's use that mode. Pick a band on which you can legally transmit. If you have a beam, point it in the direction of the sun for starters and tune across the band. Look for a DX station calling CQ, or one already in contact. (If he is already in contact with someone, make sure the contact is finished before you call.) When the station signs, give your call twice, slowly. It's best to use phonetics for the letters in your call (see the sidebar). There's no need to give the other station's call—the DX operator knows that already! The only exception might be when you are calling after a contact between two DX stations. Then you'll have to give the other station's call sign, so he knows who you're calling.

For your first contacts, try to pick stations with little accent, whose command of English seems good. After a while it gets easier to understand operators who speak English with an accent, but for now, make it easy on yourself.

If you get through, the operator will usually greet you politely. It's standard practice to lead off with a signal report, so expect that first. Two other items of information generally make up the first transmission: name and location, or QTH. These items may be given in any order, but traditionally the location is given first. The operator will then turn it over to you. In casual DX contacts, I like to give my name first, then the signal report and my location; it just seems friendlier to introduce myself first.

The second transmission is less predictable. The operator may describe his station, the local weather, or make comments about band conditions. These are cues for your next transmission. If the DX operator does not give this information, you should assume he wants to move on and make other contacts. Keep your next transmission brief. By all means, thank the operator for the contact, mention that you'd appreciate a QSL card, say 73 (*not* "73s." 73 means "best regards." 73s means "best regardses!") and goodbye. On the other hand, if the DX station seems chatty, by all means tell him about your new transceiver or antenna, and be sure to

Glossary of Terms

DX Newsletters—Newsletters featuring information of interest to DXers. DX newsletters report on the times and frequencies of operation for DX stations and DXpeditions and provide QSL routes and addresses. See Chapter 13.

THE PHONETIC ALPHABET

The International Civil Aeronautics Organization (ICAO) developed a phonetic alphabet for commercial airline pilots. Although most of the phonetics are good, some seem to hard for DX stations to understand. The following list gives phonetics that seem to work well. For some letters, more than one phonetic is given. If a station is having trouble with one letter of your call, try another phonetic.

Amateur Radio Phonetics

A	Alfa, America
B	Bravo, Boston
C	Charlie, Canada
D	Delta, Denmark
E	Echo, Easy
F	Foxtrot, France
G	Golf, Germany, Guatemala
H	Hotel, Honolulu
I	India, Italy
J	Juliet, Japan
K	Kilo, Kilowatt, Kentucky
L	Lima, London
M	Mike, Mexico
N	November, Norway
O	Ocean, Oscar (pronounced with long O)
P	Papa, Peter
Q	Queen, Quebec
R	Romeo, Radio
S	Sugar, Sierra, Santiago
T	Tango, Texas
U	Uniform, Union
V	Victor
W	Whiskey, Washington
X	X-ray
Y	Yankee, Yellow, Yokohama
Z	Zulu, Zanzibar

mention that you are a new DXer or a new ham. The latter is almost guaranteed to net you a QSL card.

Psychologists tell us that we like to hear our names used by the person with whom we are talking. Without being excessive, mention the operator's name, for example: "Well, Bela, your 100 watts and your dipole are doing a fine job here." Or, "Bela, I'm very happy to work you. You are my first contact with Hungary."

Many stations I hear working DX sound self conscious. Modulate your voice and put some enthusiasm into your conversation! Let your voice, as well as your words, convey your eagerness to communicate with this fellow radio amateur in a far-off land.

SPEAKING THE LANGUAGE

We are indeed fortunate that so many DX stations speak English, because so few of us speak foreign languages, by comparison. Perhaps you'd like to speak to DX stations in their own language. Conversational language courses are offered at many community extension schools. Learning with others is probably better than trying to learn by yourself with the aid of books and recordings. The problem with conversational language courses is, you won't be asking your next contact in Madrid for directions to the Prado museum and conversational courses don't usually include such phrases as, "You really got covered up in the QRM that time, old man." The ARRL sells a great little Spanish course for hams, called *Hola CQ*. Knowing Spanish can get you through easy contacts in Italian and Portuguese as well.

Typical DX QSOs are short, usually nothing more than an exchange of signal reports. If everyone is saying no more than "five nine," why learn a language? Well, DX doesn't always show up in pileups. Most of the nations in Africa, for example, are former colonies of various European nations. It isn't unusual for a Senegalese or Algerian operator to be speaking French, during a contact with a friend in Europe, perhaps. If you understand and speak some French, you can identify the station and call him when he's free. The number of contacts you make this way may be small, but there's no thrill like snagging a new one that everyone else has ignored because they didn't know the language. To get started, see the sidebar on Amateur Radio phrases. Several languages are featured.

WHERE TO LOOK FOR DX

DX stations can show up anywhere on a band, but there are traditional DX frequencies. They are listed in Table 5-1. The use of these frequencies (sometimes referred to in DX newsletters as "the usual DX frequencies") is not limited to DX stations or DXers, of course. You'll often hear non-DX stations operating on them.

Although these frequencies serve as the centers of DX oases, it is obvious that not all the DX can operate in one narrow segment of a band

FOREIGN-LANGUAGE PHRASES FOR RADIO AMATEURS

This pronunciation guide will help you in your initial contacts with some DX stations, but it is no substitute for language training! The phonetic pronunciations are as close to correct as possible. Your contacts will probably be happy to help you with your pronunciation.

French

0	zā-roh
1	un, une
2	du
3	twa
4	katr
5	sank
6	sies
7	set
8	wheat
9	nuf
10	dees
12	dues
17	dees-set
20	vent
30	trent
40	car-ante
73	swaz-ante trez
80	katr-vent
100	sont
1000	meel

My name is
Ma (female) Mon (male) nom ess

The QTH is ____
Le koo tay assh ess ____

Your report is ____ and ____
Votre rapport es ____ ay ____

I will send you my QSL via the bureau.
Je vooz en-vairai ma koo ess el via le bureau.
Thank you for the QSO.
Mare-ci bo koo poor le koo es aw.

I speak only QSO French.
Je parl fran-say soo-le-mon poor le koo es aw.

German

0	null
1	ein
2	zwei
3	dry

40

4	vier
5	funf
6	sechs
7	see-ben
8	acht
9	neun
10	zen
12	zwolf
17	zeeb-zen
20	zwanzig
30	dry-sig
40	vierzig
73	dry und seeb-zig
80	achtzig
100	hundert
1000	tausend

My name is
Mine nam ist

My QTH is
Mine koo tay haa ist

Your report is ____ and ____
Ir rapport ist ____ und ____

I will send you my QSL via the bureau.
Ich verde mine koo ess el cart via bureau senden.

Thank you for the QSO.
Danke shane fur das koo es oh.

I speak only QSO German.
Ich spreck doysch fer das koo es oh.

Italian

0	zero
1	uno
2	du-ay
3	tray
4	kwatro
5	sink-ay
6	say
7	set-ay
8	otto
9	no-vay
10	dee-chee
12	doe-deechee
17	dee-chee otto
20	vent-ee

30	tren-ta
40	Karanta
73	settanta tray
80	ottanta
100	cento
1000	mille

My name is
Il me-o nome ay

The QTH is
Il mepo KOO TEE ACCA ay

Your report is
Il vostro controllo ay

I will send you my QSL via the bureau.
Vi mandero la mia cartolina KOO ESS ELLE via bureau.

Thank you foer the QSO.
Molti gratzi per il KOO ESS OH

I speak only QSO Italian.
Parlo Italiano soltanto per il KOO ESS OH.

Spanish

0	sair-oh
1	uno
2	dose
3	trayss
4	kwa-troh
5	sink-oh
6	sayss
7	see-ay-tay
8	oh-cho
9	new-way-vay
10	dee-ays
12	do-say
17	dee-ayss-ee see-ay-tay
20	ven-tay
30	tren-tah
40	kwa-ren-tah
73	sah-ten-tah-ee-tres
80	oh-chen-tah
100	cien-tah
1000	meal

My name is
Mi nombre es

The QTH is
Mi KOO TAY AH-CHAY es

Your report is
Soo ra-poor-tay es

I will send you my QSL via the bureau.
Me en-vee-air-ay la tar-heta de KOO ESS-AY ELAY por el bur-oh.

Thank you for the QSO.
Gracias por el KOO ESS-AY OH.

I speak only QSO Spanish.
Hablo el ess-pan-yole solamente por el KOO ESS OH.

(although it sometimes sounds that way!). If you have some time to tune around and nothing else interesting is happening on the usual DX frequencies, it's worth looking higher in the band.

Other regions of the world have different voice allocations, which is why you hear Canadian stations on SSB in the 80-meter Novice/ Technician subband and European and South American stations in our 40-meter CW band.

The 20- and 15-meter phone bands and, to a lesser extent, the 10-meter phone band, are frequently used by missionaries overseas to make phone-patch (Amateur Radio-to-telephone connection) calls to North America. I have snagged a couple of new ones by politely and quietly calling the DX station while he is waiting for the US amateur to make the telephone call. Some of these stations are battery operated and located in the wilderness, so the QSL card may be a long time in arriving. Of course, you could buy the equipment and run phone patches yourself. This tactic might give you more leverage toward getting a QSL card!

Table 5-1
Usual DX Frequencies
CW
Near the bottom of the band or subband: 1825, 3500, 7000, 14000, 14025, 21000, 21025 and 28000 kHz.

SSB
1840, 3790, 7160, 14195, 21295 and 28595 kHz.

CALLING CQ

Let's face it: If no one called CQ, we wouldn't make many contacts. But who has the best luck with CQs? Use yourself as an example. You're tuning around the bands, looking for a new country perhaps, or just looking for a good ragchew. What criteria do you use to decide what station's CQ you will answer? The station should at least be readable. It's also nice for the sake of a ragchew if the station is speaking in a language you understand. And surely you'd like the station to be "interesting," either personally or because of location.

Now stack yourself up against all the other stations on the band. How desirable will a contact with you be to a DX station? Unless you live in one of the rarer states, your location isn't going to help you. So, what is it that will tempt a station in a country you need to answer your CQ? Probably very little, which is why most DXers don't call CQ!

That said, I'll confess that I sometimes call CQ. When I started using 30, 17 and 12 meters, I needed *everything*, so almost every QSO was a new country. When the band was quiet and I was sure I had worked every DX station that was already transmitting, I called CQ.

I also found calling CQ an effective way to round up European countries on 80-meter CW. Eighty-meter contacts count two points toward the Worked All Europe award. My 80-meter signal is strong enough in Europe to attract less-powerful stations. I *have* worked countries I needed by calling CQ. The problem I ran into was, I would get busy with a "run" of Europeans while a rarer station was calling CQ somewhere else on the band. Of course, I wouldn't know, because I was busy elsewhere. I've learned to limit "runs" to about 10 minutes. Then I go looking around again.

Directional CQ DX calls, like "CQ DX Northern Africa," are usually even less productive. Talk about bad odds!

Of course, if you just want to chat, you can take pot luck and send out a CQ DX, but the odds favor a response from a not-very-rare country. But there's nothing wrong with chatting. Whether you chat or hunt depends on your goals. If your goals include working new countries, your best bet is to look for them.

Chapter 6

Goal Setting

If you are the competitive type, you already practice goal setting, although you may not be aware of it. Setting short, intermediate and long-term goals motivates you to keep trying. Achieving your goals is equally important. Nothing diminishes interest faster than failure. Set reasonable goals—goals that are not too easy, but definitely possible.

One obvious goal is achieving DXCC (100 DXCC countries confirmed). Depending on your station and available time, this goal could take two days, two months or two years. (Two days is *not* a reasonable goal!)

If you can put in three or four hours a week at the radio, you can work 100 DXCC countries in less than a year. Set your goal for 10 months. But to keep yourself interested, set intermediate goals of, say, 25 countries in three months and 50 countries in six months. If you have never made a DX contact, your first goal is to do so. Another good short-term goal is qualifying for the IARU Worked All Continents (WAC) award.

After you've worked 100 DXCC countries, you'll want to keep going and work more, but you can set some other goals, too. Making the contacts necessary for the Worked All Zones or Worked All Europe awards are two examples.

Don't compare your progress with someone else's. We each have individual needs and abilities (not to mention equipment and opportunity) and we have to live in the real world. DXing is a sport, a hobby, an avocation. You can't allow it to interfere with your responsibilities to school, job or family. It's easy to become mesmerized by the pursuit of new countries, especially when you work a new one every time you sit down at the radio. But there must come a time when you "pull the big switch" and get back to the other, important parts of your life.

Although serious DXers want to work every new country that comes on the air, sooner or later we all miss a couple. Okay, you'll feel rotten and maybe you'll feel like you failed. Success in DXing, however, is not limited to working every station you call. If you gave your best effort and did all you could during the time you had, you succeeded.

One method many competitors use to increase their performance is *visualization*. There are several intricate rituals in use, but the idea is to "see" yourself accomplishing some goal you desire, such as getting that DXCC award. You may wish to purchase and hang the frame in which you'll display the award (11 × 14 inches) and picture the certificate in place on your wall. Instead of counting sheep at night, you can count QSL cards from the countries you need. Rehearse successfully getting through in a pileup. But don't spend *all* your time visualizing; you have to get on the air to make the contacts that count for DXCC, too!

Chapter 7

SSB or CW?

During periods of above-average propagation conditions, Novices and Technicians will find more DX on 10-meter phone than on either of their 15- or 10-meter CW subbands. But, as go the sunspots, so goes 10 meters. When solar activity is low, the 15-meter Novice/Technician CW subband is more productive. Novices and Technicians should not overlook their CW subbands when the sun is active either, because some choice DX occasionally shows up there. (Beginners in other countries have to study the code, too.) And, because activity in the Novice 15- and 10-meter CW subbands is lower than in the 10-meter phone band, there is less competition and a greater chance for a QSO. Further, if you are really interested in DXing, you need a higher class of license and the ability to sling out the dits and dahs.

This opinion is not just the raving of an old-time CW nut! I could fill three books with the gory details of DXpeditions and other rare ones I have called for hours on SSB, when I just couldn't break the pileup. When the DX *finally* got on CW, I often got through on the first call. SSB receivers use wider bandwidths by necessity and all the other strong signals calling simply overload the automatic gain control (AGC) circuit. CW allows the use of much narrower filters. Also, a good CW operator develops the ability to separate signals in his brain. This ability is no mystery, because with CW we're dealing with single tones, not a mishmash of voices.

If you have a General class license or higher, you can operate on the other HF bands not available to Novices and Technicians. There, you should also concentrate on CW, especially if you don't have a big signal. True, some of the rarer DX stations sometimes operate in the Extra Class subbands, but a majority of those operators listen higher in the band, where General and Advanced class amateurs can transmit. If you get hooked on DXing, the first time you hear a really rare station working in the Extra Class subband, you'll be surprised how fast you can get your code speed up to snuff! Meanwhile, you can readily work more than 100 countries without going into the Extra Class subband.

What about SSB? True enough, there is plenty of DX on SSB. Almost every country I hear people fighting over on SSB, however, I have easily worked on CW (and usually on more than one band). Enough said. CW is a different means of communication and no one masters it overnight. Most of us old-timers couldn't wait to get on phone (in the days when Novices were limited to CW). Many of us found our way back to CW again, though, simply because we like it better. No matter how wild the pileup may be on CW, it just doesn't *sound* as bad as even a low-key pileup on SSB.

Even SSB-only operators have an incentive to get their code speed up, if only to pass the Extra Class exam. There is always something happening in the Extra Class phone subbands and you won't want to miss it.

Why is there so much DX on CW? Most American radio amateurs can afford a rig that works both modes, but this isn't true in many foreign countries. In many parts of the world, amateurs can't buy commercial equipment at any price and obtaining crystal filters and other parts necessary to build SSB gear is difficult, if not impossible.

There, CW is the only mode available. You won't work these folks on any other mode. CW is harder at first; you know how to speak with your voice—now you must learn to speak with your key. I am not suggesting you give up SSB. Quite the opposite: I am hoping you won't give up CW. Being flexible is the mark of a true-blue DXer.

GETTING BY ON CW

Let's say you decide to take the plunge and you're listening on a CW subband. Suddenly, you hear a bunch of stations sending their calls for a few seconds, spread out over several kilohertz. Then, just as suddenly, all is quiet. You tune lower in frequency and hear a weaker signal sending "5NN" ("N" is an abbreviation for "9"), but it sounds more like a machine-gun burst. There's your DX station. Who is it? Stick around, you'll hear the call sign soon enough. Now he's calling another station, but you can only copy part of the call sign because he's going so fast. If it were your call sign he was sending, would you recognize it? If not, no sense adding to the QRM by calling him. Find another station. But for now, let's say you can follow what he's sending. There he goes again, he just sent "TU." That's his way of acknowledging the other station's report. He's listening up the band for another call now—yes, he just let loose with another burst. Wow, you really have to concentrate!

Why not listen above him, and see if you can find the station he's working. There's someone else, sending at the same machine-gun speed, sending his call at the end of his report. Okay, back to the DX station again. A few contacts later, you've got his routine figured out and you can copy most of what he's sending.

Assuming your license allows you to transmit on this frequency, why not give him a shout? From listening, you know about how long he listens before he picks out a call. And you know whether he tunes up, down, or randomly after each contact. Here's a hint: If you send your call a little slower than he's sending, he might slow down when he calls you. Sometimes a slowly sent call sign stands out in a pileup of fast callers, too. Why not? Okay, you say, here goes: "KR1S." Nope, someone else got him. Let's see, the station he called was a little lower in frequency than me. Guess I'll stand pat for one more call. Here we go again. "KR1S." Yikes! He just called me! Gosh, "5NN de KR1S TU." He sent "TU." I guess he heard me. Not exactly long winded, is he! Oh, yeah, what was his call sign? I figured it out a few minutes ago and wrote it down...here it is. Okay, put it in the log and don't forget the UTC time and date. Hey! I just worked a new one on CW! Gee, that wasn't too bad. Where'd I put that W1AW code-practice schedule, anyway?

Chapter 8

Propagation and Antennas

Y ou've probably noticed you can hear stations from certain parts of the world on 10 meters at only certain times, or that 10 meters is most usable for DXing during the day and early evening, while the lower-frequency bands are often usable all night. Of course, there are times when none of the MF/HF bands (160-10 meters) are usable. Radio propagation is a lot like the weather. It varies from hour to hour, day to day, and season to season. There are long-term trends as well. Like the weather, radio propagation can be predicted to a certain extent, but not controlled. The mysteries of propagation are studied with great interest by scientists and radio amateurs around the world, but they can also be very frustrating! Mark Twain said, "Everybody talks about the weather, but nobody does anything about it." All DXers talk about propagation, but the best we can do is try to understand it. Just as you plan for seasonal changes in the weather, you can plan for changes in radio propagation.

THE IONOSPHERE

Radio waves travel in straight lines. Unless some reflective object gets in the way, a radio wave travels in a straight line for millions of miles. Because we live on a round planet, direct radio communication over the horizon is impossible without some reflective object overhead. Fortunately, no one told Guglielmo Marconi about this, or he might never have tried his trans-Atlantic experiment in 1901! Following Marconi's surprising (at the time) success, scientists had to determine *why* he succeeded. While radio amateurs inspired by Marconi's work were *using* the ionosphere, the scientists were studying its physics.

The ionosphere is formed when ultraviolet and X-rays from the sun knock electrons loose from some of the gas atoms in the Earth's upper atmosphere, resulting in *ions* (molecules from which electrons have been dislodged) and "free" electrons. X-rays require about eight minutes to travel from the sun to the earth and only the daylight side of the Earth is subject to this ionizing radiation. As a hemisphere passes into darkness, the free electrons begin to recombine with the ionized atoms.

Radio waves penetrating a layer of ionized gas are *refracted,* or bent, like light waves passing from air into water. How much they are refracted depends on the intensity of the ionization, the frequency of the radio waves and the angle at which they enter the layer. In speaking of propagation, we frequently refer to "reflection" from the ionosphere, as though it were a mirror.

The ionosphere includes several layers or regions in the upper atmosphere. They are called the D region, the E layer, and the F layer. At the top is the F layer. Although the F layer sometimes separates into two layers, called F1 and F2, we'll talk of them as a single layer. The

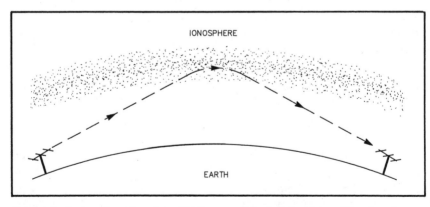

A lot of what makes Amateur Radio possible is because radio signals can be refracted by the ionosphere, the layers of ionized gases surrounding the earth.

F layer is responsible for most DX propagation. Depending on the intensity of its ionization, the F layer can refract frequencies up to about 70 MHz, above the 6-meter amateur band. The highest frequency the F layer can refract is known as the maximum usable frequency, abbreviated MUF. The MUF is dependent on ionization intensity. The MUF at a given place in the ionosphere increases from dawn to noon, then slowly decreases. At sunset, recombination begins, and the MUF drops throughout the night. Somewhat lower than the F layer is the E layer. Most of the time the E layer doesn't do much for the DXer. Sometimes a form of propagation called "sporadic E" occurs, which provides strong, short-range (up to about 1500 miles and, rarely, 3000 or more miles) 10-meter propagation. Sporadic-E propagation, also called "E skip," commences suddenly, usually in the evening. It is most common in the early summer, but can occur anytime. During a sporadic-E opening you'll hear strong signals suddenly pop out of the noise. A few minutes later they may disappear, to be replaced by other strong signals. A sporadic-E opening is a good time to work some new states or Central American countries. It is usually not a good time for lengthy ragchews!

Closest to the Earth we find the D region. It's called a region because it doesn't form into an identifiable layer. Because solar radiation must penetrate the farthest to reach it, the D region doesn't become as heavily ionized as the F layer. While the F layer slowly recombines through the night, the D region recombines quickly at sunset. During daylight hours however, the D region *absorbs* radio frequency energy. The degree of absorption depends on the intensity of ionization and decreases as the frequency increases.

With this understanding of F-layer MUF and D-region absorption, we can draw the conclusion that we'll get the best results operating on the highest frequency the F layer will refract. Lower frequencies will also be refracted by the F layer, but will suffer greater absorption in the D region. At night, when the D region disappears, the recombining F layer may not support 15- or 10-meter propagation. On 80 and 40 meters however, the DX is rolling in—even though these bands are generally useless for DX during daylight hours.

THE FOUR SEASONS

The earth's elliptical orbit around the sun means the distance to the sun varies from 92 million miles during the northern hemisphere winter to 94 million miles during the northern hemisphere summer. During our winter months, solar radiation is somewhat stronger, but is concentrated on the southern hemisphere. The Earth's axis is somewhat tilted and its angle to the sun varies throughout the year. Thus, the sun's highest angle above the horizon is greater in summer than in winter. The beginning and ending dates of our seasons are determined by the sun's overhead position. On approximately June 21 and December 21, the sun is at its respective farthest north and farthest south positions. About March 21 and September 21, the sun is directly over the equator. Propagation to different parts of the globe is greatly affected by the changes in seasons.

THE VARIABLE SUN

Astronomers refer to our sun as a variable star. Although its visible light output is fairly constant, its output at the wavelengths that affect propagation is definitely not. Radio amateurs and scientists have observed that propagation conditions seemed to vary in an approximately 11-year cycle, which coincides with variations in the number of visible sunspots. Sunspots are cooler, darker regions on the sun's surface that may be areas of high magnetic fields. Whatever causes them, they increase and decrease in number about every 11 years. When there are more sunspots, the sun radiates more of the energy that enhances F-layer propagation and the MUF increases to 50 MHz and higher. When there are very few sunspots, on some days the MUF may not reach 14 MHz. During the sunspot peak in 1990, the first 6-meter DXCC awards were completed.

RADIO STORMS

Not all solar radiation is beneficial to radio propagation. Sometimes the sun's surface erupts in a flare, which reaches thousands of miles in height. Flares often produce radiation that result in propagation *blackouts*. A sudden ionospheric disturbance (SID) occurs soon after a flare. It starts quickly, lasts a few hours, then goes away. When a SID begins, signals fade rapidly and you may think your receiver is broken! SIDs only affect the side of the earth facing the sun; thus, they only happen during daylight hours. SIDs affect propagation by increasing ionospheric absorption. During a SID, the higher-frequency bands may still be open, although signals will be weaker. If 15 meters seems dead, try 10 meters.

Geomagnetic storms, on the other hand, are caused by slow-moving solar particles. They begin a day or more after a flare. Geomagnetic storms settle in slowly and may last for several days. During a geomagnetic storm, the polar regions are most affected. Sometimes the ionization around the poles is so intense that a visible aurora occurs. Propagation paths through the polar regions are usually blocked. Signals that travel near the polar regions sound "watery," as they are modulated by the rapidly fluttering auroral curtain. Geomagnetic storms have less effect on lower-frequency signals and it is often possible to work DX on 160 through 20 meters. For the most part though, conditions are usually poor. After you've been through a couple of ionospheric storms, you can easily see why commercial and military long-range communications have been largely shifted to orbiting satellites.

OTHER PHENOMENA

Long Path

If you have a globe, try to find the place on the other side of the planet that is exactly opposite your location, or *antipodal* to you. The distance between these locations is the same, no matter which direction you turn. There will, however, usually be only one best path for propagation between the two points. When you are trying to work into a part of the world that is almost antipodal to you, the shortest distance may be on the order of 11,000 miles. This is called the short path. If it is daylight at both locations and the long path (opposite direction) is completely in darkness, the long path will often provide stronger signals. If the station you're trying to work doesn't have a directional antenna and you do, you just have to turn your antenna 180°. If the other station has a directional antenna aimed toward the short path, you'll probably be better off working short path. The best way to find out is to turn your antenna!

Gray Line

Gray line is the name given by radio amateurs to the terminator between sunlight and darkness. For every location there are terminators

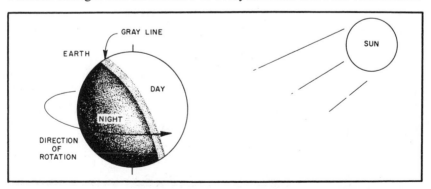

The gray line is the transition region between daylight and darkness. One side of the earth is coming into sunrise, and the other side is just past sunset.

each day (except in polar regions). Propagation is usually enhanced between locations on the edge of a terminator and between locations on different terminators. For example, between a location where the sun is rising and another where it is setting. Because of the earth's tilt, the terminator path varies throughout the year. There are gadgets and computer programs available that graphically depict the terminator's position. They are certainly educational and can help you understand why a band opens to certain parts of the world when it does.

PROPAGATION DIFFERENCES BY BAND

As you've already seen, propagation is subject to so many variables that it's impossible to simply state what the conditions are like on any particular band. But each band does display certain general characteristics. So, with the warning that the following descriptions are necessarily general in nature, here's a band-by-band summary of radio propagation.

10 and 12 Meters

Our 10-meter band is the one most affected by the sunspot cycle. During cycle peaks, 10 is open almost every day, often late into the night. When the sunspots are lively, 10 meters is the place to be! In the mornings, propagation is best to the east, moving to the west throughout the day. At night, even during low sunspot activity, 10 is usually open along north-south paths. Because D-region absorption is low and multielement 10-meter beams are relatively small, it's possible to work plenty of DX with a 10-W rig. Sporadic-E propagation often brings after-dinner treats on 10 meters, when stations from a few hundred or more miles away suddenly barge into your local roundtable.

Because the 12-meter band is a little lower in frequency than 10 meters, it stays open a little longer and is the place to head for when 10 meters closes down.

15 and 17 Meters

Fifteen meters is an interesting band. Although high enough in frequency to be affected by the sunspot cycle, 15 usually opens a little earlier and stays open longer than 10 or 12 meters. When the sunspots decline, 15 is a good summer band if the MUF can't make it to 10 meters. The first Novice DXCCs were worked on 15 meters, when Novices were required to use crystal-controlled transmitters (no VFO!) and were limited to 75 W input and one-year, nonrenewable licenses.

20 Meters

If you're a Novice or Technician DXer looking for a reason to upgrade, listen to 20 meters! Twenty meters is the Times Square of Amateur Radio: Spend enough time there and you'll meet everyone you know! During sunspot-cycle peaks, 20 is open all night, all over the world. Even during lulls in solar activity, 20 opens just about every day. The down side of its popularity is that the activity level is high and many DXers build large antenna arrays specifically for 20 meters. The competition is much tougher on 20 meters than on 15 or 10. The high level of competition only becomes a factor when the occasional rare country shows up. You'll find plenty of good DX to work on 20, without much hassle. As your skill improves, you'll find that a modest station can still work the tough ones. And there's no better place to learn your skills than 20 meters.

30 Meters

I singled out 30 meters because it's the only band on which US hams are restricted to less than 1500 W out, except for the Novice/Technician subbands. Propagation conditions are quite good, so 30 is a good place to hang out when you need to get away from the rat race for a while. It's a very casual band and one on which you can compete as an equal without an amplifier.

40 Meters

The best DXing on 40 meters is usually right around sunrise and sunset (when D-region absorption is low), although 7000-mile contacts at night are commonplace. The trouble with 40 meters at night is that it's filled with shortwave broadcast stations, which obliterate the Novice/Technician subband. During periods of low solar activity, the nighttime MUF sometimes struggles to reach 7 MHz, and 40 may be the only DX band open. During the day, 40 suffers from D-region absorption, although the East Coast usually starts hearing European stations a couple of hours before sunset. When 40 is open, a simple vertical antenna performs well.

80 and 160 Meters

Like 40 meters, 80 and 160 meters are open for DX from sunset to just after sunrise. When the sunspots are rare, 80 and 160 are popular. On some nights during periods of low solar activity, the MUF may only get as high as 2 MHz (yes, it gets that bad). DXers call 40, 80 and 160 meters the "low bands." Avid low-band DXers stay up late and get up early!

PROPAGATION CHARTS

Charts of predicted propagation conditions appear monthly in *QST*.

These charts are prepared in advance, based on presumed solar activity for the month in question. Charts are provided for communication between three geographical areas of the US and major geographical areas of the world.

Each chart has three graphs. The first depicts the highest possible frequency (HPF) over a 24-hour period, the second charts the maximum usable frequency (MUF), and the third shows the optimum traffic frequency (FOT). See April 1983 *QST*, pp 63-64, for a detailed explanation.

The ARRL Operating Manual contains propagation charts for a wide variety of solar conditions, covering a 12-month period. Propagation

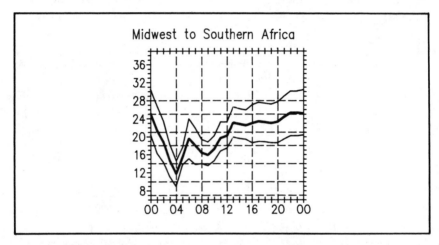

Midwest to Southern Africa

Although propagation charts can't predict *exact* band openings, they can tell you when a band opening is most likely to occur. This is one of several propagation charts found in QST each month. See text for details.

charts are useful if you're setting up a schedule with a DX station, or if you want to know what band would provide the best shot at a DX-pedition. The DXpedition may not be on that band at that time, however! Besides, just because the chart says 15 meters is the best band for propagation to a country you need, other bands may provide usable communications as well. As DXers, we have to work the stations where we find them, not where we'd like them to be. What the charts do give you is a general idea of what you might expect to hear on a given band as the day progresses.

I heard YS/N5TW on 20 meters this morning. I'm working on my 17- and 12-meter DXCCs, and need El Salvador on both bands. A quick glance at the chart told me the propagation to Central America might be good enough for a contact on both bands, so I asked Peter to QSY. We were feeling the effects of yesterday's solar flare; signal strengths weren't fantastic, but we got through just the same. DXpeditions interested in working into different areas of the United States can use the charts to determine the best times and frequencies. They're certainly educational and informative, but they can't take the place of on-the-air experience.

ANTENNAS

Signals striking the ionosphere at shallow angles are propagated better than those striking at higher angles. Signals at very high angles may not be propagated at all. Because of the effect of the ground beneath your antenna, your signal begins to climb as the wave moves farther away. The amount of climb is referred to as the *radiation angle* of the antenna. The radiation angle is determined by the antenna type, height above ground, and ground conductivity. In general, the higher the antenna the lower its angle of radiation. Generally, vertical antennas have lower angles of radiation than dipoles, unless the dipole is quite high in terms of number of wavelengths.

In practical terms, the higher you can install the antenna the better. For dipoles and beam antennas like quads and Yagis, a half wavelength or higher is the rule of thumb. If you can't get your antenna up a half wavelength, put it up as high as possible.

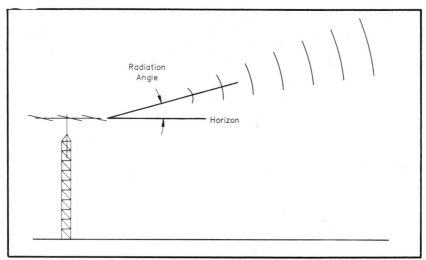

An antenna's radiation angle is important for determining its suitability for DXing. Generally, antennas with low radiation angles work best for DX contacts, whereas antennas with high radiation angles work best for local or stateside contacts. See text for details.

Dipole Antennas

A dipole antenna is made from two quarter-wavelength pieces of wire. The feed line, usually coaxial cable, is connected to the center. Dipoles are known as *balanced* antennas. Coaxial cable is not balanced, which can result in some current flowing on the outer shield of the feed line. This current distorts the radiation pattern of the antenna somewhat. If the cable runs near a TV antenna, the radiated signal may cause interference. To remedy the situation, many amateurs use a *balun*, a transformer that makes the antenna think it's connected to a balanced feed line. Baluns are often built directly into the center insulator, which makes installation easier.

Dipoles are usually suspended between two vertical supports, but there is no reason why they can't be installed vertically if necessary.

The radiation pattern of a dipole more nearly matches the classic shape when the antenna is ½ wavelength or more above ground. This is difficult to achieve with 80- and 160-meter dipoles. As is the case with all antennas, put it up as high and in the clear as possible. I worked more than 100 countries on 80 meters with a dipole only 35 feet high. I won't brag about the signal reports, but the QSL cards still count for DXCC!

A dipole fed with coaxial cable will work as a dipole only on the band for which it is cut. Using a tuner to nullify the standing-wave ratio (SWR) will only disguise the mismatch. RF *has* to go somewhere, so you will radiate and receive, but this is not an ideal situation.

Back in the days before coaxial cable, everybody used *balanced feeders*, which were nothing more than two pieces of wire with insulating spreaders to keep them equally spaced. Also known as open-wire line, this type of feeder has an impedance range of 150 to 600 ohms. Transmitters back then could be adjusted to match that impedance, or a tuner was used.

My 80-meter dipole fed with open-wire feed line works well on 40 and 20 meters as well, but I have to reset the antenna tuner when I change bands.

Because a dipole antenna has an impedance of about 72 ohms, the mismatch of impedances between open-wire feed line and the antenna is severe. However, open-wire line has less loss than coaxial cable. That still leaves the problem of matching high-impedance balanced feed line to the low-impedance (52 ohms), unbalanced output of modern amateur equipment. Here's an ideal application for an antenna tuner. You hook one up between your rig and the open-wire line feeding your antenna, and away you go. Well, most of the time.

Open-wire feeders radiate some RF, into the atmosphere, and into your shack. Some modern solid-state equipment is affected by RF fields. Electronic keyers, computers and packet radio TNCs often go wild when operated close to open-wire feed lines. The solutions to these problems could fill several books, so if your open-wire feeders cause havoc in the shack, you'll probably have to use monoband dipoles fed with coaxial cable.

Antenna Tuners

When balanced feed lines were the rage, antenna tuners were designed differently than most units available today. *The ARRL Antenna Book* and *The ARRL Handbook* cover this area in greater depth, but a short discussion is appropriate here. Today's antenna tuner is usually a simple impedance-matching circuit, like an L or pi network. Older tuners used air-wound transformers with taps on one winding to change frequency. The difference between them is, the air-wound transformer was used to match a high-impedance balanced line to a low-impedance rig. Modern tuners frequently use a transformer wound on a ferrite core.

Ferrite-core transformers are more compact than their air-wound equivalents, but the core may saturate if the mismatch is great, especially if you're running a power amplifier. When the core saturates, it radiates energy at harmonics of your operating frequency. This harmonic energy probably causes many of the problems with keyers and computers. I have one tuner of each type in my shack. When I use the old-style, air-wound coil tuner, I have no problems. When I use the other tuner, especially on 15 and 10 meters, my keyer and computer go wild.

Vertical Antennas

Vertical antennas are ideal for limited-space installations and are usually good DX performers. Unless you have some very tall trees, you'll probably get better results on 160, 80 and 40 meters with a vertical than you will with a low dipole. Most verticals, however, require *radials*, which are wires laid around the antenna, usually on or just below the surface of the ground. If you think of the vertical radiator as one half of a dipole, the radials become the other half, or other pole. Generally speaking, the more radials you use, the better a vertical antenna performs on long-distance paths, the kind DXers are interested in. A multiband vertical requires separate radials for each band. You can bury the radials just below the surface of the soil, or snake them around trees and shrubbery, but they are absolutely necessary. Without radials, DX performance is greatly reduced.

If you elevate the base of a vertical, you can get away with fewer radials. A simple single-band vertical made of wire suspended from a tree limb, with its base 8 feet or more above ground (so no one walks into the radials) will perform quite well with only two to four radials.

At least one commercial half-wavelength multiband vertical does not require radials, which makes it ideal for locations where even a single radial is undesirable.

Beam Antennas

Just what *is* a beam antenna? Well, before we can discuss that, we should talk a little about nondirectional antennas. The most-common non-directional antenna used by hams is the simple vertical. Although the pattern of vertical can be distorted by nearby objects, for now let's assume that it radiates equally in all directions.

Now consider the dipole. Dipoles do not radiate equally in all directions, although if they are low enough they appear to. The rule of thumb for dipoles is to install them ½ wavelength or more above ground. On 10 meters, this is only about 17 feet, but on 80 meters it's 132 feet! Experience shows, however, that an 80-meter dipole, 40 feet above ground, is somewhat directional.

The directional pattern of a dipole favors some directions over others.

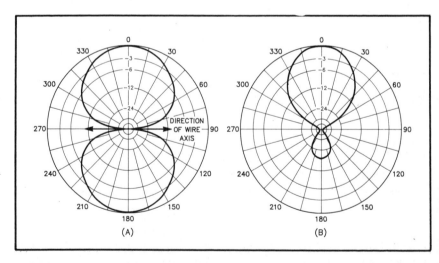

(A) shows the representative radiation pattern of a dipole antenna. Under ideal conditions, the pattern is symmetrical and bidirectional. At (B) is the representative radiation pattern for a beam antenna. Note that signals coming from behind and from the sides of the beam are greatly attenuated, while signals from the desired direction are enhanced.

If we compare our perfect vertical with our perfect dipole, we see that for certain directions the signal radiated by the dipole is stronger than that radiated by the vertical. However, the vertical is stronger in the null directions of the dipole.

What if we could turn the dipole? We would now have a simple directional antenna. Rotatable dipoles are popular on 15, 12 and 10 meters because they are easy to build. They do offer advantages over fixed dipoles and verticals. Notice that a dipole radiates equally in two directions. One is the desired direction, but the other is not.

We need something to cut off the response to the back and enhance the response to the front. This is the principle of the Yagi and the cubical quad. Both antennas use a *driven* element (to which the feed line connects) and one or more *parasitic* elements to concentrate the beam's radiated energy. The driven element of a Yagi is usually a dipole with an impedance-matching device.

Cubical quads use loops instead of dipoles. Concentrating the beam's radiated energy really makes a difference in performance. Remember, this increased performance helps on receiving *and* transmitting.

Beam antennas have many specifications. The one we tend to look for first is the *gain*, which is a measure of how much of the beam's energy is concentrated in the forward direction. Unfortunately, it is practically impossible to accurately measure the gain of an HF antenna. The ARRL recognizes this and gain figures for antennas are not published in advertisements in League publications.

Another quality of a beam is its front-to-back (F/B) ratio, a measure of how much it rejects signals coming from behind. Rejection of signals coming from behind can often make the difference when you're trying to dig out a weak DX station. F/B ratio and gain are adjusted by varying the spacing between elements and the lengths of the elements themselves. The same tuning that results in maximum gain does not provide the best F/B ratio. All beam antenna designs are a compromise between these two important factors.

Monobanders and Tribanders

The Yagi and quad were originally intended for use on one band. A single-band beam is called a monobander. Monoband beams provide the best overall performance, but limit you to operation on only that band. Triband Yagis and quads use multiple driven elements or *traps* to resonate the antenna on three bands.

Triband antennas often have six or more elements, but not all elements are active on all bands. A typical 6-element triband Yagi may have four active elements on 10 meters and three active elements on 15 and 20 meters.

Tribanders are heavier than comparable 3- or 4-element monobanders. Element spacings are necessarily a compromise as well, resulting in somewhat less gain than is available from a monobander. Tribanders offer you the advantage of having only one antenna to install and maintain. The performance difference between the better triband antennas and 3- or 4-element monoband Yagis is noticeable, but slight.

Yagis and Quads

The debate over whether quads outperform Yagis has been going on for decades. Quad lovers can present scientific data that proves their antenna is better and so can Yagi lovers. The big problem with quads is that they are difficult to install and maintain. If you live in an area prone to ice storms, a quad is probably not a good choice.

Because the driven element of a quad is a closed loop, it acts like a short circuit to rain-induced static, a real problem with some Yagis. Quads usually have a greater bandwidth, meaning you can cover more of the band with a low SWR. Quads are generally quieter receiving antennas than Yagis.

CHOOSING A TOWER AND ROTATOR

When you've decided on an antenna, you need the right rotator and tower to go with it. No one ever had a tower or rotator that was *too* big, but there is no sense in overdoing it, either. Antenna specifications include surface area, measured in square feet. Your tower and rotator should be rated to handle somewhat more surface area, to allow for the surface area of the mast, and also for ice loads if necessary. A coating of ice greatly increases the surface area (and weight) of an antenna.

Installing a tower is no job for the inexperienced. You can't do it *safely* alone. Ask around to find some help from local DXers who have done it before. Never install a tower where it can fall on power lines. And *never* climb without a safety belt.

BEAM HEADINGS

Aiming a directional antenna with the help of most world maps will send your signal in the wrong direction! All you need to confirm this is a small globe and a piece of string. Hold one end of the string on your location, and pull the other end to some part of the globe you'd like to talk to. What you're seeing is the ''great circle'' path. This path is usually quite different from the path indicated on a flat world map. For example, on the average map, Western Europe appears to be due east of the Northeastern US, but the shortest great-circle path is actually to the northeast.

Antenna rotators are calibrated in degrees, like compasses. The center of the scale is usually at the north, although "south-center" scales are available. You'll recall from geometry that a circle can be divided into 360°. For direction-finding purposes, true north is considered to be 0°. East is 90°, south is 180° and west is 270°.

Directional antennas have a property called *beamwidth,* which you can visualize like the beam from a flashlight. The beamwidth is usually calculated or measured so that at the outer limits, the power of the beam's radiated signal has dropped to half its value at the center. Most good HF beams have typical beamwidths of about 30°. Therefore, you'd like to be within 10-15° of the exact bearing when you point your beam.

Aiming a beam is best done with the aid of a compass, but you must account for magnetic declination. The magnetic north pole is some distance from the geographic north pole. Different locations in the United States have different declinations. That is, the difference between what a compass says is north and what really is north varies between locations. Camping supply stores sell topographic maps which indicate the magnetic declination for the areas they cover.

Now that your beam is properly aligned, how do you know where to point it? You could use your globe and string, but fortunately, more convenient methods exist. *The ARRL Operating Manual* lists beam headings to all DXCC countries from various points in the US. Unless you have a *very* directional beam, using the bearings from the city closest to you will suffice for all but the nearest countries, such as those in the Caribbean. Nearby countries are usually louder anyway, so this is not such a handicap.

The *Operating Manual* also contains *azimuthal equidistant* maps centered on various cities, which give you a different perspective on the world! Australia is that lump to the left, and Antarctica is the one on the bottom. If you are putting up a fixed-position, directional antenna such as a wire beam and you have a choice of headings, the map will help you maximize its usefulness. You can see at a glance what parts of the world will be within your beamwidth. Custom azimuthal equidistant maps are available for any location from several suppliers listed in the *Operating Manual* and *QST.*

One further note about using directional antennas. A band may be open in more than one direction, although signals on the other paths are weaker. We have a tendency to listen for only the loudest signals. By doing so, we may miss weaker signals coming from other directions. It pays to investigate other paths besides the strongest one; some truly rare DX might be yours for the taking!

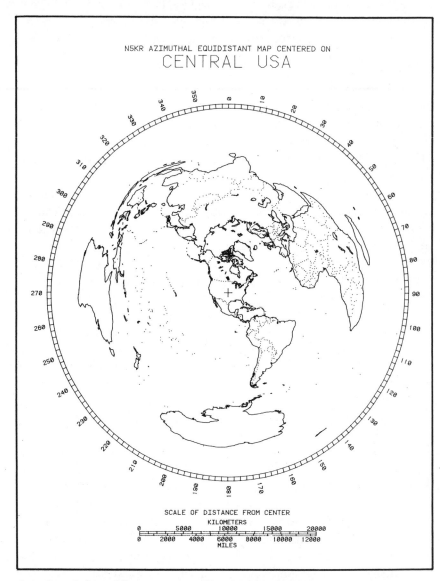

An azimuthal equidistant map, while showing a somewhat unusual projection of the globe, is perfect for quickly determining beam headings. When compared to conventional projections, several interesting characteristics are apparent. For example, from the central US, the short path beam heading for Europe is about 30°, not due east as it appears on many conventional maps.

Chapter 9

Sending and Receiving QSLs

W hen I opened my mailbox tonight, I found a half-pound package of QSLs from the bureau. I also found two cards from a DXpedition to Mongolia last fall and one from Chad.

I'm still sorting the bureau cards, but I've already discovered several new ones for my Five-Band DXCC and even a couple of all-time new ones. One bureau-sent card I was especially glad to see was from SU1RR. I worked him in a contest last year, and sent my QSL directly to Egypt, as directed by the *Callbook*. The American guest operator sent his cards through the bureau. It looks like I didn't even have to send a QSL card for this one. That's pretty unusual.

To get the cards from Mongolia and Chad, I sent the following to their respective managers: my QSL; an envelope addressed to me; a dollar bill, also known as a "green stamp."

In the past, many DX stations automatically sent you a card through the bureau. If you were in a hurry, you could send one or two International Reply Coupons (IRCs) with your card directly to the station. There weren't as many DX stations then, nor as many QSL managers. Of course, there weren't as many DXers, either.

With so much more DX activity nowadays, sending QSLs is a big expense for an active DX station and takes a great deal of time. Many DX operators have limited spare time, which they prefer to use operating (fortunately for us!) rather than answering QSLs. Thus, the QSL manager.

The DX station sends his logs to his manager. You send your QSL to the manager. The manager checks your card against the log. If he finds your call in the log, you'll get a QSL. That is, if you sent an envelope and sufficient return postage.

If you live in North America, DX stations will rarely spontaneously mail QSLs directly to you. Stations permanently located in the more common countries will often send you a card through the QSL bureau, but many of them will do so only if they receive yours first. If you want to receive, you first have to send!

YOUR QSL CARD

Your QSL card should be visually attractive, without being complicated. Some QSLs look more like resumes, with lists of awards and clubs. Keep it simple. Sure, you're proud of your rig and your accomplishments, but will the DX station take more than passing notice of such information? Photo QSLs are great, except most of them place your call sign on one side and the report form (date, time, frequency, etc) on the other. A busy DX operator may forget your call sign in the time it takes to turn the card over. Result: Your call is incorrectly entered on the card you receive. If you have a two-sided card, be sure your call sign appears in large type on both sides. However you have them printed, use standard postcard size (3.5- × 5.5-inch) stock.

On the other hand, be sure you don't make mistakes when filling out your own card. Of course, you'll always use UTC time, but make sure the date agrees. If you live in Chicago, 6 PM Central Standard Time is midnight UTC. So, for the contact you make at 6:15 PM, you write 0015 UTC. No problem there. But, if it's December 31 in Chicago, the UTC date is January 1. Check the date to avoid making an error. If the station you worked has made many contacts, the operator or his manager may not bother to look in the next day's logs when they can't find your call sign.

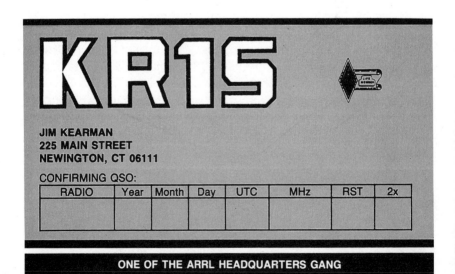

A simple, uncluttered QSL card with space for all of the QSO information on the front is ideal.

On the subject of dates, there is an international standard method of entering dates. The order is YEAR, MONTH, DAY. Don't spell out the month, as only those who read English will know what you mean. Use Arabic numbers for the day and year and Roman numerals for the month: 93 VI 5 means the fifth day of the sixth month, 1993. Note that if you had written 6/5/93, it could be interpreted as June 5 or May 6. Placing the month ahead of the day is not standard in all countries, however. See the Roman numerals in Table 9-1 if you need a refresher.

QSL VIA THE BUREAU

If you aren't in a big hurry, you can save money by QSLing the countries you hear every day through the bureau (see the sidebar). Save your air-mail stamps and dollar bills for the less common countries and DXpeditions. In fact, operators in some of the more common countries don't seem to respond to direct requests for QSLs. One European country, which I thought would be easy to confirm, absorbed a princely sum in green stamps before I finally received a QSL card.

IRCs AND GREEN STAMPS

So the story goes, one IRC is good for one unit of postage anywhere IRCs are accepted. The *Callbook* contains a table detailing how many IRCs are necessary to mail an air mail postcard or letter from each country that accepts them. Be prepared for a shock—some countries have exorbitant postal rates. IRCs are not cheap in the US, either. IRCs are

Table 9-1
Roman Numerals for Months

Month	Roman Numeral
January	I
February	II
March	III
April	IV
May	V
June	VI
July	VII
August	VIII
September	IX
October	X
November	XI
December	XII

QSL Via the Bureau . . .

In these days of increasing postage costs and overall inflation, there's still an inexpensive way to send QSL cards to, and receive QSL cards from, DX stations—the Incoming and Outgoing QSL Bureaus. As you might expect, the Outgoing Bureau forwards your QSL cards to similar Bureaus in most overseas countries; the Incoming Bureau is where you claim QSL cards sent to you from DX stations.

For $2 per pound, the ARRL Outgoing QSL Bureau will ship your QSL cards to similar Bureaus throughout the world, which are typically maintained by the national Amateur Radio Society of each country. Cards may be sent to the Bureau up to 12 times per year. Considering that 150 average QSL cards make up a pound, the savings in postage is tremendous. Although QSLing via the Bureau usually takes longer than going direct, it's still the preferred method for most DXers, especially for QSLing the more common DXCC countries.

You must be an ARRL member to use the Outgoing QSL Bureau. Send an SASE to ARRL HQ, 225 Main Street, Newington, CT 06111 for the latest information on which countries are served by the Outgoing Bureau.

The ARRL Incoming QSL Bureau (there's one for each call district in the US and Canada) is where you can claim QSL cards sent to you by DX stations. ARRL membership is not required to use the Incoming Bureau.

DX QSL cards are sent to the various Incoming Bureaus and are sorted by call sign suffix. To claim your cards, send a 5- × 7-1/2-inch SASE to the Bureau serving your call district. Print your call sign neatly in the upper left corner of the envelope. Most Incoming Bureaus will sell you the required envelopes and postage for a small fee.

Don't send envelopes to your "portable" Bureau. For example, NTØZ/1 sends envelopes to the WØ Bureau, not the W1 Bureau.

The Incoming Bureau will keep your cards for about a year after they arrive. So be sure to claim them on a regular basis, or they'll be thrown away!

Send an SASE to ARRL HQ at the address listed above to request complete information on the Incoming and Outgoing QSL Bureaus.

---

redeemable for less than half their purchase price (you buy them at the post office), but you can often buy them at or slightly above redemption value from QSL managers and other sources that advertise in DX newsletters.

Green stamps are US one-dollar bills. As I write this, the post office price for an IRC is about $1 and it takes two IRCs to buy as many stamps overseas as can be purchased with one dollar. If the country to which you're sending the card allows its citizens to have American currency, you're obviously better off sending a green stamp. China, for example, does not allow citizens to have Western currency, so IRCs are necessary there.

REGISTERED MAIL

Unfortunately, postal workers in some countries routinely open over-seas mail and remove money or IRCs. Your QSL card may or may not be delivered after the other contents are stolen. To increase the chances of your QSL card being delivered complete with enclosures, you can send the envelope via Registered Mail. The cost is quite high compared to regular air mail however, so I only use it when there's no other way to confirm the country.

QSL MANAGERS

QSL managers act as agents for DX stations. DX stations send their logs to their managers. DXers send their QSLs to the manager. When the manager receives a card, he checks the logs. If the two agree, the manager fills out and sends a card to the DXer. Some managers serve more than one DX station. Sometimes the manager *is* the DX station. For example, K1TN is also VP2MDC. QSLs for VP2MDC are sent *via* K1TN, who wears a QSL manager's hat while at home. If you want a direct response from a manager, you must supply a self-addressed envelope and sufficient funds to pay for return postage. If a manager handles more than one station, it's better to send a separate envelope for each. Managers don't drop everything when they receive a request; they put all the requests for each station together and work on them when they have time.

QSL DIRECT

Finally, you may be able to send a QSL directly to the DX station. This is sometimes tricky if you're sending IRCs or money, as local postal employees may routinely open incoming mail and remove your IRCs or dollar bill, as mentioned earlier.

Be sure you address the envelope correctly. Never send a card overseas by other than air mail. Take the time to find out if the country to which you're sending the card can use IRCs, or if its citizens are prohibited from having Western currency. Take pains to conceal the contents of the envelope by using "privacy" envelopes (a pattern on the inside of the envelope makes it harder to detect the contents), wrapping a piece of opaque paper around your QSL card and enclosures and taping the seal on the envelope so it can't be easily opened. Do not write the DX station's call sign on the outside of the envelope—it can attract unwanted attention.

For contest QSOs with more desirable countries, where a direct QSL is indicated, getting the card there quickly may make a difference. If the operator only kept one copy of the log, you want your card to arrive before he sends the log to the contest sponsor.

It sometimes takes many months and often years to get a QSL. If you sent yours to a manager and your return address was on the envelope, no news is not totally bad news. The QSL manager has to wait for the DX station to forward the logs. At least you haven't received your card back stamped "NOT IN LOG." It takes several months for cards to start coming through the bureau. Once they start, if you're active you'll find they come at regular intervals. Sadly enough, sometimes you just never get a card and you never know why. All you can do is try to work another station in that country, and hope for better luck.

PIGGYBACK QSLS

A common practice of some DX stations is to send more than one station's QSL in an envelope. They hope the recipient will forward the other cards to the stations whose QSLs went along for the ride. This practice explains why we sometimes receive cards with strange return addresses, or don't receive answers to our direct requests. If you receive a packet of cards in this manner, at least forward them to ARRL HQ, where they will be sent out via the Incoming QSL Bureau system. This courtesy will cost you very little. If you haven't received an answer to a direct QSL request after a year or so, try again, and mention your previous, unfulfilled request. Politely ask that your card be sent directly to you this time. It doesn't hurt to offer to forward some cards for the station.

Chapter 10

Pileups

Although new countries are occasionally added, the number of countries on the *DXCC Countries List* hovers around 325. Of these, about 225 are fairly easy to work. Once you have worked most of them, you have to *work* for the new ones. By work I mean planning to operate when it's sunrise or sunset on the other side of the world; scanning the newsletters to determine if a station you need has an operating pattern; and entering the battleground of the pileups.

Pileups are tough if you don't have a big signal (and sometimes even if you do). Assuming you aren't running 1500 W to a large Yagi, you can still succeed if you use your head, most particularly your ears!

Here's 5H3TW, in Tanzania, a country you need. You hear him passing out signal reports, but you can't hear the stations he's working. It may be that he's working some other part of the world; you can determine that by listening to him. If he's calling one JA (Japanese station) after another, he's obviously not listening for US stations. Make a note of when and where you heard him, and move on. If he's calling US stations however, you should be able to hear most of them on scatter or short skip.

If you don't hear them, it's because 5H3TW is working split, listening 2 to 10 kHz or more above his transmitting frequency. If you zero beat and call him, you're defeating his purpose of keeping his frequency open so he can be heard clearly. And, because he isn't listening there anyway, he won't hear you. Here's a rule that should be printed in red on every ham license: Never transmit until you have determined where the DX is listening! This may take time, often several minutes, if the pileup is large. Your first impulse is to throw your call sign in there right away. Maybe you'll get lucky. This unreasonable faith in luck supports lottery ticket sales, but it only causes needless QRM on the ham bands. I can fantasize about winning the lottery or I can work for a living. In a pileup, DXers invest their time, they don't waste it. Here's how.

5H3TW will send a station's call and a report. With your second VFO, look for that station. You'll hear several stations blindly sending their calls at the same time, and with any luck you'll find a station sending a signal report, perhaps even signing a call. Now you know where 5H3TW is listening. Set your VFO a little higher, then switch back to the VFO that's set to his frequency. If you're using a transceiver, make sure the split function is enabled! When you hear 5H3TW acknowledge the QSO (usually just a "TU"), send your call once. If he doesn't call you, switch VFOs and find the station he called. Reset your VFO and try again. Sometimes a DX station listens on both ends of the pileup, where the QRM is a little thinner. If you are listening, you'll soon know. Then you can slip down to the other end of the pileup and call there.

Even though you are on the right frequency, you don't always get through, because other DXers know these techniques too. Given time and reasonable propagation, you will prevail. For example, it took me about an hour and a half to work XW8CW on 20-meter CW. Most of the problem was sifting through the stations who were calling blindly, often 15 kHz away from the frequency where XW8CW was listening! Eventually I found a clear spot near the frequency of the last station XW8CW worked, and got through. After 90 minutes of tracking and calling, I was pretty surprised when I heard him sending my call!

I find that most stations send their calls three or more times. I don't have a big signal, so I have to be tricky. I send my call once. More often than not, the DX comes back to me while most of the pileup is still calling.

WHEN THE DX IS LISTENING ON HIS FREQUENCY

Some DX stations never operate split. Maybe their rigs won't allow it, or they don't know how. This is called operating "transceive." Getting through a big pileup to a station operating transceive is tough. Such events are a major reason for all those big single-band beams and 1.5-kW amplifiers you hear about. When several SSB stations are calling on one frequency, the result is a loud hiss, like white noise. The DX station's receiver is incapable of detecting a signal in the pileup unless that signal is about twice as strong as any other.

If you spend some time listening to a pileup, however, you'll notice that there are occasional "holes," where for a brief instant, fewer stations are calling. If you can slip your call into one of those holes, you can often get through, even if you're not the loudest signal in the pileup. Does that ever feel good! By the way, this technique is useful when you're trying to get on a list for a DX station. Nets and list operations are, after all, operating transceive also. Holes usually open up after everyone has been calling for several seconds or longer. It pays to hold your tongue (although this trick works on CW, too) and wait for an opportunity. It helps to be using VOX (voice-operated transmit, rather than push-to-talk, or PTT), and to have quick reflexes.

Setting your transmit frequency a little below center is sometimes helpful, because it gives your voice a higher pitch. Sometimes the higher pitch helps cut through the pileup. Don't go too far off frequency, or you'll be outside the passband of the DX station's receiver.

The worst part of a transceive pileup is wondering if the DX has called someone while you're still calling him. You can't always tell, because so many other stations are also still calling and they may be much louder than the DX. You usually find out when you hear another station giving a report to the DX. Pileups always seem to have a pattern, where the DX station takes a certain length of time to pick out a call and give a report. Time your calls accordingly, but don't be surprised if someone chews you out for calling too long. You might feel foolish, but your interference was accidental. The station chewing you out on frequency has no excuse! Ignore the insults; that station didn't get through, either.

COPING IN PILEUPS

DXers may claim to love pileups, but there isn't one who wouldn't rather work a new one on the first call. Locher's *The Complete DX'er* will teach you how to improve your chances in a pileup. But even that excellent handbook cannot prepare you for the goings on in a big pileup.

Pileups are dynamic, almost taking on a life of their own. A good analogy is a medieval battlefield—strictly hand-to-hand combat, with broadswords and maces. You are a knight on a quest, without a shield! It's not bad enough that you have to wait for someone to put a rare country on the air and hope that good band conditions coincide with a lull in your work and family obligations. No, there are many fire-breathing monsters and Black Knights to overcome as well.

For example, we find XW8CW transmitting on 14.025 MHz and listening over the range of 14.030 to 14.040 MHz. XW8CW finishes working WB2EDW and looks for another contact. One hundred stations call and XW8CW picks out WA1WVK's call. When the DX station calls WA1WVK, you would expect all other stations in the pileup to wait while WA1WVK makes his transmission. This is not only polite, it's sensible. If anyone is transmitting on top of WA1WVK, XW8CW will not copy 'WVK and will have to ask for a repeat. It is very unusual for a DX station to give up once he or she copies someone's call. So instead of making 200 contacts an hour, XW8CW's rate drops to less than 100. Given that rare DX stations, especially on DXpeditions, have limited operating time, you can see that this tactic (if you can call it that) *lessens* everyone's chance of getting a QSO. And if XW8CW is listening at 14.033 and you're transmitting on 14.039, he won't hear you anyway!

The smart move is to look for the station just called by XW8CW, so you can call on or near that station's frequency when the time comes. This is all well and good, but when 50 stations are blasting away, it's hard to find the one who got the QSO. In a big pileup you won't be able to find that station very often. Do the best you can. Sometimes you'll find it, and you'll know where the DX station is listening at the moment. Most DX operators tune higher in frequency as they work through the pileup. They sometimes move back and forth, or work off the top and the bottom. You have to listen to find out.

If you only know approximately where XW8CW is listening, there's another tactic you can use. I know this one works because I actually used it to work XW8CW. When he stood by, I switched VFOs and tuned to the area of the pileup where I knew he was listening. (I heard a station he worked in that general area a few minutes earlier and my listening taught me that he usually worked through a pileup one small area at a time.) I tuned back and forth a little bit to find a somewhat clear frequency (there *are* holes in pileups). Then I switched VFOs again and quickly sent my call. In a very large pileup, the DX station usually needs several seconds to dig out another call, which gives you time to pick your opening. While this tactic won't work every time, it improves the odds over randomly sending your call. Most of the people calling in a pileup are counting on luck. People do win lotteries and luck sometimes wins QSOs, but the surest route to success is via the good old work ethic.

Policemen

One of the major hassles in a pileup is the so-called "policemen" or "cops." Some are self-appointed judges, too. Policemen send "UP UP" when someone transmits on the DX station's frequency when the DX is working split. Judges send "LID LID" and often worse under the same conditions. Let's just call them "regulators." Calling them policemen is derogatory to our public servants. The vehemence of their remarks is directly proportional to the rarity of the DX. The problem with regulators is their timing, or lack thereof. Let's say W1XZ hears 3Y5X stand by for calls and doesn't know that they always operate split. Yes, he should have had a look around before calling, and yes, it was hard to *miss* the Bouvet pileups, but he calls anyway, right on 3Y5X's frequency. He stops calling to listen for an answer and the regulators start their litany of "UP," "LID LID," and "(expletive deleted)." Simultaneously, 3Y5X, oblivious to the imminent riot on his transmitting frequency, comes back to someone in the Midwest, who may or may not be able to copy 3Y5X through the melee. The first wave of regulators doesn't hear 3Y5X, because they're transmitting right on top of him. When they stop, the second wave starts questioning their intelligence and birth status. The first wave then feels obligated to escalate. In a few seconds, 14.025 is transformed into the radio equivalent of a barroom brawl. Meanwhile, 3Y5X keeps handing out reports to those still able to copy him.

It is sorely tempting to unleash your frustration at people who call on the DX station's frequency, or at the regulators, especially when you think 3Y5X *might* have called you. If you do, to paraphrase Bob Dylan, you become your enemy in the moment that you speak. Novelist John Barth wrote that every person attending a wedding thinks he or she is the most important person there. Pileups are more comparable to some marriages than they are to weddings perhaps, but the attitudes expressed by each participant in a pileup surely indicate that everyone thinks he or she is *it*.

I hope this won't ruin anyone's day, but you should remember that the pileup would go on just fine without you, be you regulator or merely one of the knights questing. Becoming regulators gives frustrated knights a *sense* of control, but most of the time they only make the situation worse. There's nothing you can do to modify another person's behavior, but you can control yours. Regulators are a nuisance that successful DXers learn to live with, like power-line noise, QRN, and ionospheric blackouts.

Finally, you have to cope with the Black Knights, who intentionally generate interference on the DX station's frequency. Black Knights resent the members of the wedding party, so they commit acts of vandalism to somehow compensate for their diminished self image. Feeling that the DX station would never hear them, or lacking the perseverance to give it a try, they transmit where they are sure to be heard and acknowledged. You cannot directly modify their behavior either, but by totally ignoring them you effectively take away their existence.

Out of hundreds or thousands of stations in a pileup, one or two may be intentionally interfering, one or two may be calling on the wrong frequency, and five or six may be acting as regulators. The jammers, the uninformed, and the regulators are not calling the DX. They have *chosen* to withdraw from the quest and they won't get a QSO. Not all stations calling the DX will get QSOs either, but how would you rate the odds? Which group do you want to join?

Sometimes the situation on the DX stations's frequency gets so bad you can't copy the DX at all. You need the country, propagation is good, but you can't hear through the mess. What do you do? Spend some time with your family, take a walk or read a magazine. The people causing the problems often get tired and go away. You can try again later. If you want to stay by the radio, have a look around the bands. A good pileup tends to attract all the attention. Other countries you need may be calling lonely CQs, waiting for you to find them.

HE CALLED ME—WHAT DO I SAY?

When you get through in a pileup you need only send your call, a signal report and a "TU." The thank you serves as a combination "73" and "K." When the DX is sending only a signal report, don't slow things down by giving your state or, worse, your name. The DX is trying to maintain a rhythm, to work as many stations as possible during his allotted time. Your name and QTH will be totally ignored as the DX tries to keep focused on the task at hand. In other words, "599 TU KR1S" is enough. On SSB, say "KR1S, Roger 59" or "KR1S, 59 Thanks." Giving your call sign helps the DX station confirm that the station he called is the one giving the report and also fulfills the FCC identification requirement.

HOW DO YOU KNOW FOR SURE?

If this pileup is the only game in town, you may decide to hang in for a while. When anarchy (or a burst of static) strikes the DX station's frequency, how can you be certain that the DX came back to you, and if he did, that he copied your report? Well, you can't. A good DX operator is consistent. After receiving each report, he may send "TU," for example. If you weren't sure you were the station called and your exchange was as long as the station he did call, you could mistake someone else's "TU" for yours. To avoid this uncertainty, have the best receiving system possible. Good filters, quiet receiving conditions, and the best antenna you can manage are worth millions when the DX is weak. It also helps if you can concentrate well and have some experience copying weak signals. Sooner or later, one of your QSL cards will come back marked "NOT IN LOG." That's part of the game and it should strengthen your resolve to improve your station and your operating skills.

If you think the DX station might have copied your call incorrectly, it doesn't hurt to repeat it a few times, slowly and with clear phonetics. If one letter is wrong, use two or more different phonetics for that letter. Then, ask the station to confirm your call: "Please confirm, my call is Kilowatt Radio One Santiago." Not every DX station will acknowledge your worst fears by repeating your call to you, but at least you know you did all you could.

If you think the DX station got your call wrong, stay in the pileup and make another contact. There is nothing wrong with doing so. It is somewhat unsporting to make two contacts back to back, to "make sure you are in the log," but not if you have a reasonable doubt.

If you're sure the DX station copied your call sign and information correctly, however, you should forego making additional "insurance contacts." Analysis of the logs of one DXpedition showed that about *half* of the contacts were with stations who had already worked the DXpedition on that band and mode. Many DXers were unable to get through because of the extra congestion.

Chapter 11

DX Nets and Lists

N ets are groups of hams who meet on designated frequencies at specified times. Some nets are social gatherings, some handle traffic. Other nets bring DX stations and DXers together to exchange information and make contacts.

If you've listened on the 40, 20 or 15-meter phone bands, you've no doubt heard the "Echo Tango Net," "Snooky's Net," or one of the other popular DX nets. Or perhaps you've heard a DX station asking for "last two letters only." DX nets and list operations are an integral part of DXing. No one ever brags about working a new country on one of these operations, but the truth is, many hams do work many new countries on nets. In some cases, the country may be unworkable any other way.

WHY LISTS?

Through the 1960s, the cost of a voice transmitter (in those days, AM was more common than SSB, transceivers were rare) was about twice that of a CW-only transmitter with the same power output. With its standard abbreviations and better weak-signal performance, CW was the mode of choice when one's financial resources and knowledge of other languages were limited. Since 1970 however, taking inflation into account, the cost of an HF SSB transceiver has steadily declined. Less-expensive equipment made phone operation accessible to more people, both in the US and abroad.

With the economic hurdle surpassed, there still remained the problems of weak signals and language barriers. A 100-W SSB signal is harder to copy than a 100-W CW signal, especially when the operators at each end speak different languages! Another problem with early SSB transceivers was their inability to transmit and receive on frequencies more than a couple of kilohertz apart (at best). Prior to the introduction of transceivers, everyone had separate receivers and transmitters and working "split" was the norm. When a rare DX station running one of the new transceivers called CQ, the answering pileup completely obliterated his signal and no one knew to whom he was replying. Enter the "net control."

At some point, a DXer who spoke both the language of the DX station—and that of the majority of stations calling him—came riding in on his white horse and offered to act as a go-between. The first step was to take down a list of stations wishing to work the DX. That done, the go-between called each station in turn, permitting him to call the DX station. Somewhere along the line the "net control" also became the official judge of whether the contact was "good." More on this subject later.

Eventually, hams whose daily routines permitted regimented activity began to set up "nets," where DX stations and their suitors would congregate, and the net control would perform his services for more than one DX station at a time.

Some DX stations with a good command of English and reasonably strong signals even bypassed the net control altogether and began taking lists for themselves.

Some readers may wonder what benefits the DX station gets from a list or net, where another station arranges the contacts and judges their authenticity. Well, if they hit the right nets, DX stations can pick up new states and countries too, and perhaps learn a bit of English along the way, while they save up for a better antenna system. The point is, for many hams, operating in DX nets is their introduction to Amateur Radio.

On the other side of the coin is the DXer, typically from a Western country, who is picking up new countries on nets, rather than "freestyle." Without the struggle of hunting for that new one, then getting through the pileup, what is the incentive for this mutation of DXing? This is only my opinion, but let's face it, Western society is numbers oriented, and to the DXer, there's only one number: the number of countries confirmed. Before you can confirm them you have to work them, and nets can help you work DX you wouldn't otherwise get. Nets can benefit even those who don't use them to work new countries. The French DX Foundation Net for example, is an excellent source of information on DXpeditions and other items of interest to DXers.

Of course, you have to get on the list before you can work the DX, and that's where one of the touted advantages of nets is disproved. Net aficionados sometimes claim that nets give weaker stations a chance they wouldn't have in a pileup. But you have to be louder than anyone else to be heard by the net control, so what's the difference? No, weaker stations don't benefit from nets. The advantage of nets is that they are like DX watering holes. If you consistently make the rounds you can consistently pick up new countries. In some cases, a country may be available only on a net. If you need that country, you can try to get on the list or wait (perhaps forever) for someone who works freestyle to visit the place.

GETTING ON THE LIST

DX stations "check in" to a net, others "get on the list." What constitutes DX largely depends on the net control. Some nets consider anything outside the United States and Canada to be DX. A station from a common country will often check in after a list has been taken, then get to work the DX before anyone on the list. This practice is especially frustrating to US and Canadian hams who have waited patiently, sometimes for hours, for their turn. But that's the way it is. If you are outside North America, you can probably get in when the net control asks for DX check-ins, unless "rare DX" is specified. If you are in North America, you have to wait for the net control to take a list. Depending on how rare the DX is, this may be done by call areas, countries, or just plain free-for-all style. Listen and follow the rules. If you don't, you may be ignored by the net control and you won't get the contact you want.

Sometimes the net control specifies that the list is for stations that need the DX "for a new one, never worked before on any band." Maybe you've worked this country before but never got a QSL. For the most part, your conscience is your guide. At least one net control, however, maintains an on-line data base of check-ins and contacts. If you work the same station or country twice on that net, when the list was for first-timers, you won't be welcome the next time you show up!

Let's use the fictitious "North Atlantic Net" as an example. This net meets every day at 1400 UTC on 21.325 MHz. The usual net-control station lives on the East Coast of the US. DX stations wishing to make

---

REGULARLY SCHEDULED DX NETS

These are some DX nets that are accessible to North American stations. Starting times are approximate, and may vary depending on season. Nets usually run as long as there is DX to work. Information on other DX nets (or new ones) can be found in DX newsletters or by asking other DXers.

Name	Days (UTC)	Times (UTC)	Frequency MHz
Africana Net	Monday-Friday	1800	21.355
Arabian Nights	Friday	0500	24.250
E-T DX Net	Daily	2000	14.160
Family Hour	Daily	1200	14.2265
247 DX Group	Daily	2230	14.247
256 DX Group	Daily	2000	14.256

Seasonal and propagation-related changes in days, times and frequencies may occur.

a few contacts, and who have propagation to the East Coast, check in with the net control, W2XYZ. W2XYZ then asks for non-DX check-ins, usually from North America, the Caribbean and South America. (Other nets cater to other parts of the world at times when propagation is favorable to those areas.) Everyone interested in working one of the DX stations on hand tries to check in, usually by giving the last two letters of his or her call sign. When the net control has a "list" of 10 or so "last two letters," he "runs" the list.

The last two "letters" of my call are actually "1S," or "One Sugar." When the net control calls One Sugar, I call the DX station of my choice. (If the net isn't busy and no really juicy DX is on board, I may be allowed more than one call, but it's best to ask first.) I give my call, and a signal report, assuming I've heard the DX station working someone else already. If not, I delay the report until the DX station comes back to me. The DX station acknowledges my call and report, and gives me a report. I acknowledge that report ("Thanks for the five four") and enter a new one in my log. If the DX station or I make an error in the call or report, the net control will ask for a repeat. When we both have the exchange correct to the net control's satisfaction, he or she pronounces it a "good contact," or just "good one."

When the list-taking starts, stations are asked to give the last two letters of their calls, for example, "One Sierra." I have noticed that there are frequently two or three stations whose calls end in the same two letters, which can make for problems when the list is called. If you find you share the same last two letters with another station that frequents the nets, you might want to pick two other consecutive letters in your call, and use them. Be consistent, however, so you don't appear to be pulling a fast one, and remember the letters you used!

A problem faced by hams in the first and tenth call areas occurs when the net control hears and writes "one" or "zero," but reads them as "I" or "O," especially with single-letter suffixes! If the net control calls "India Sierra" and no one responds, I politely ask, "One Sierra?" I haven't lost yet. Be honest, though. If the net control asks for "Echo Tango" and your call is KC0OT, don't jump in and call the DX.

If the station being run is rare there will be many stations calling the net control. If the list is being taken randomly and not by call areas, the net control will usually take 10 to 20 partial calls, run them, then take another group. If conditions are good and the DX station can stick around for a while, you can probably get on the list eventually, even if you aren't very loud. The first 10 seconds are the worst. If you aren't a big signal, wait for everyone to take a breath, then make your call. Like any pileup, those on a list or net ebb and flow. Good operators learn to anticipate the lulls and time their calls to fall into them.

Sometimes the net control reads the list, so you know right away if you made it. I have waited more than an hour, though, only to discover that I was not one of the chosen. If you don't make the list, don't go away mad. Stick around for a while and see what's happening. Study the net control's procedures so you'll be better informed next time. And, frankly, the carrying-on can sometimes be very entertaining, especially to the un-involved eavesdropper! When the net control has taken some arbitrary number of partial calls (anywhere from five to fifty), the list is "run."

YOUR TURN

The net control is running the list and your turn is coming. Get ready! If you have a rotary antenna and the DX and net control are in different directions, you have to determine the beam heading for the DX station. You should have already heard the DX, so you know if you need to point short path or long path. And you know you can hear him well enough to make a contact. If you can hear the net control with your antenna pointed at the DX, that's the best bet.

It doesn't hurt to make up a cue card, so you know what to do when the time comes. When you're called, say "Thank you," so the net control knows you heard him. If you have to turn your antenna, say "Swinging the beam," and do so. Remember, the DX station already knows his call sign. If there is only one DX station on the net, there's no need to repeat the call. Just say, "This is," and give your call sign phonetically, slowly. Use common words, either the ITU standards or some other accepted phonetics (see Chapter 5). Give your call twice and use the exact same phonetics and pronunciation each time. Words longer than one syllable sometimes get through better under poor conditions, but only if the DX station knows the word! Slow down! Then give the station his signal report, slowly. Enunciate each number carefully, so a five doesn't sound like a nine.

Unless you live in a city or state that you know has personal meaning to the DX station, don't bother with that data. The DX station probably doesn't care. Giving your name is another time waster. This isn't an audition for the Rag Chewer's Club; communicate, don't converse.

Now all you need to do is copy his acknowledgment of your call sign, his report and your signal report. If conditions are good, no problem. But when the DX station is weak, this can be very trying, especially if the station speaks English with an accent. If you absolutely can't hear the station, admit that and ask to be put at the end of the list. The net control will usually respect your honesty and do so.

If you aren't sure of your report, don't guess. If you copied the first number as "5," ask for the second number again. Usually the DX station will then count out the number or numbers. This makes it easy if you've been paying attention, because you just count the number of syllables you hear; when the DX station stops counting you've got the number.

If you don't respond when the DX station turns it back to you, the net control will say "Over." If you still don't know for certain, ask for a third attempt. I've never heard that request denied. Don't try to fake it. Sometimes the interference quiets down, the ionosphere perks up and there's your second number. If you don't have it after the third try, ask to be put at the end of the list. You never know.

Now you have to prove the contact is valid. Assuming your call and report were properly copied, all you have to do is thank the DX for your report: "Thanks for the 5 and 1." Put some enthusiasm in it! Some stations sound like they'd rather be anywhere but on that list when they acknowledge a report. Maybe they're embarrassed. Why be embarrassed? Everyone else on frequency is there for exactly the same reason. Let the DX station know you are sincerely glad that he or she sat through the drudgery of copying yet another call and report, just so you could have another piece of bragging material!

If you copied your report correctly, someone will likely sound off with "good one," meaning you passed the test. If you didn't give the right answer, the net control will usually ask the DX to give you the report again. While this intervention speeds things up (the net control is probably louder than you), it is the reason for much of the controversy surrounding such operations.

In freestyle operating it's up to you to make sure the DX station has properly copied your call. Beyond that, what constitutes a "good" contact is pretty much up to you and the DX station. No one is going to help you, but neither is anyone going to judge you. If you hear ZA9XYX calling CQ and call him, and he copies nothing into his log except your call, is that is good contact? Well, if you receive a QSL from ZA9XYZ confirming that contact, who is to say it wasn't?

In the world of lists and nets, however, you must ensure that the DX correctly copied not only your call, but also his report. Then you must be sure that you correctly copied your report, or the on-scene judge, the net control, will not vouch for the QSO.

Suppose the net control says that the contact was no good, because you could not copy your report. Do you write for a QSL anyway? Again, this is principally a matter of conscience. If the DX station is handling his own QSL duties, or is sending his log to a manager, you might get a card. If the manager is on frequency and keeping his own log, however, you're out of luck. The contact that might have flown freestyle is no good on the net. Chances are, though, if you can barely copy the station on a net, you never would have made a freestyle contact anyway. And the net control will do everything possible to help you communicate the required information, short of giving it himself.

SHOULD YOU WORK DX ON NETS AND LISTS?

Sound easy? It is! Sound *too* easy? Some DXers think so. They refer to net operation as "spoon feeding" and "fishing in a barrel," and say many nasty things about nets and those who work DX on them. But you can bet that most of the critics have worked at least one country on a net that they've never worked elsewhere!

Keep in mind that list and net operations are legal, and the QSLs count for DXCC, just as much as those you fought for in pileups. The difference lies in your personal goals. If your goal is to run up your countries-worked total, working nets and lists should be *part* of your game plan. If you work at home, for example, and don't have time to tune around looking for freestyle operations, leaving the rig tuned to a net is a good way to pick up a new one here and there. When something you need shows up, you can take a break and try to get on the list.

If you have time to spend with the radio, however, you can often find more desirable countries by carefully tuning the bands that are open (don't forget 30, 17 and 12 meters), and working freestyle. Many times I've worked a couple of goodies on CW or SSB while stations are lining up to get on a list for some fairly common country. Of course, working DX freestyle usually requires a rig that can work split. If your transceiver can't do that, you may have to get most of your new ones on nets and lists. Often, though, you'll come across choice DX working transceive, listening and transmitting on almost the same frequency. You don't know until you look.

Regardless of their relative merits, nets and lists should be reserved for DX that can't readily be worked any other way. What with all the planning and list taking, you might spend two or three hours waiting to work one country. If you have worked just about everything else that's available, this is time well spent. If you have worked fewer than 200 countries, you could be investing your time more effectively by scouring the bands for other new countries. Yes, you can work more than 100 countries by methodically moving from net to net. In the same span of time you could easily work 175 countries freestyle—and have more fun besides.

As far as working a DX station from one of the more common countries, it's probably easier in a net, simply because you don't have to tune around looking for the station, and the other stations on the net don't need that country. Of course, one advantage of working hams in commonly heard countries freestyle that you can *talk* to them! On a net, there's no chance to chat. When the occasional rare DX station shows up on a net, the pileup is murder. Often, the word has been spread in advance, so a couple of hundred DXers are calling at once, trying to get on the list. Everyone would have a better chance if the DX station went elsewhere and called CQ. Unfortunately, some DX stations never seem to appear anywhere but on their favorite nets.

Sometimes DX stations take their own lists, acting as DX and net control. For a couple of minutes there is a frenzy on the frequency, as a ton of DXers repeat their "last two," then everyone sits around while the DX works the stations on the list. I suppose this technique gives the DX station an occasional break from the blasting pileup, but it is very boring for the DXer. I'd rather see the pileup continue because it gives me something to do; it keeps the edge sharp. Private list-taking is also confusing for those who happen by while the DX is nonchalantly working stations, because there's no pileup. The temptation is to drop your call in when the last DXer signs. Last time this happened to me, someone else on frequency read me the riot act! I guess his edge was still sharp.

I am no stranger to nets and lists, and I have worked many countries for the first time on nets. While preparing this book, I checked my records and found I had worked 47 countries for the first time on nets. With only four exceptions, however, I have since worked all those countries again freestyle. I didn't work them a second time because I felt the net contacts were tainted. I usually worked the country again on CW (all the DX nets I am aware of are on SSB), or on another band.

DX nets are useful sources of information as well, although, like any other medium, sometimes the information is wrong. Tips on upcoming DXpeditions, QSL routes, postal information (such as which countries' mail is routinely "searched"), schedules with other stations and the like, can be gleaned from listening on a net. If you work at home, listening to a net is at least as entertaining, and certainly more interesting, than daytime television! In the evening, a net makes a pleasant background to puttering in the shop—sort of an "all-news" format for DXers.

DX nets are a part of Amateur Radio, and you *can* work DX on them. You may wish to make them a part of your operating time as well, but don't afraid to throw your signal into the pileups, even if you're running only 100 W and a dipole. If you are serious, you have to try to work every country that comes along. Most DXpeditions never take lists or check into nets. Get some experience working in pileups now, so you have a better chance at a rare one in the future.

Chapter 12

DXing in Contests

Many DXers are also contesters, but for me, contests have only one function: They provide concentrated DX and the chance to work new countries. There are hundreds of contests throughout the year, most of which are announced in *QST*. Some of the most productive contests for DXers are the ARRL DX Contests, the ARRL 10-Meter Contest, the IARU HF World Championships, the *CQ* World-Wide DX Contests and the Worked All Europe Contest. There are many other regional contests that are also useful, but the contests mentioned can bring you dozens of new countries, even if you don't have a big signal. See Table 12-1 for a list of major DX-oriented contests.

The contest announcements in *QST* will give you the basic rules for each contest and will explain the required contest exchange. The exchange is what you send to the DX station and what the DX station sends to you. In the ARRL DX and 10-Meter contests, for example, US and Canadian stations send a signal report and their state or province; the DX station sends a signal report and serial number. In the *CQ* World Wide contest, everyone sends a signal report and *CQ* Zone number (there are 40 in all). The continental US encompasses three zones, so make sure you know which one you're in!

Be sure you know the correct exchange before you call a station operating in the contest. You may not be competing, but others are, and it isn't fair to bog them down with questions or an incorrect exchange. Worse yet, you'll hear stations giving complete QSO information, like name, location, weather, and so on. Then the contester has to ask for a serial number, zone, or whatever! Serious contesters get used to this sort of thing, but if you want a QSL card, you might want to consider the impression you made during the QSO!

When DXing during contests, instead of trying to make as many contacts as possible, you'll be looking for new countries. Contests are also a good way to build up your "band/countries" total for 5BDXCC. For the most part, DX contesters don't work very wide splits, as the bands

Table 12-1
Major HF Contests for DXers

Month	Contest	Scope	Exchange	Details in:
Feb	ARRL DX Contest, CW	W/VE stations work DXCC countries	Signal report and state or province	Dec *QST*
Mar	ARRL DX Contest, phone,	W/VE stations work DXCC countries	Signal report and state or province	Dec *QST*
Mar	*CQ* WPX (prefix) contest, phone	All stations can work each other	Signal report and consecutive QSO number	Contest Corral, Feb *QST,* or Jan *CQ*
May	*CQ* WPX (prefix) contest, CW	All stations can work each other	Signal report and consecutive QSO number	Contest Corral, Feb *QST,* or Jan *CQ*
Jun	All Asian DX Contest, phone,	Asian stations work all others	Signal report and age	Contest Corral, May *QST*
Jul	IARU HF World Championships	All stations can work each other	Signal report and ITU zone	May *QST*
Aug	All Asian DX Contest, CW	Asian stations work all others	Signal report and age	Contest Corral, May *QST*
Aug	European DX Contest, CW	EU stations work all others	Signal report and consecutive QSO number	Contest Corral, Jul *QST*
Sep	European DX Contest, phone,	EU stations work all others	Signal report and consecutive QSO number	Contest Corral, Jul *QST*
Oct	*CQ* World-Wide DX Contest, phone,	All stations can work each other	Signal report and *CQ* zone	Contest Corral, Oct *QST,* or Sep *CQ*
Nov	*CQ* World-Wide DX Contest, CW	All stations can work each other	Signal report and *CQ* zone	Contest Corral, Oct *QST,* or Sep *CQ*
Dec	ARRL 10-Meter Contest	All stations can work each other	Signal report and ARRL section	Nov *QST*

are too congested. Send your call, copy the exchange and send your exchange, and off you go. That's the bright side. The bad news is, some DX stations don't QSL contest QSOs. So, if you need Senegal and you hear *another* 6W, work that one too. If you think the country is unusual enough that you don't want to wait for another one to come along, add "PSE QSL" to your exchange. The station may jot your call down separately, or give you the call of his QSL manager if he has one.

Start out on the highest band that is open. If that's 10 meters, start out at the low end and identify every station you hear. If you need it, work it. If the pileup is heavy or the station just can't hear you, note the frequency and come back later. Pileups draw attention and thus feed themselves, and the rapid changes in band conditions are never more noticeable than during a contest. A half hour later you'll probably get through on the first call.

Keep moving. When you've tuned across 10 meters, check 15, then 20. Then go back to 10. It doesn't hurt to occasionally check the other modes, too. For example, if you're working a CW contest, check the SSB subbands once in a while. Remember, you're not looking for contest points, you're looking for new countries. Single-operator stations often jump from band to band, spending a few minutes on each looking for multipliers before moving. If you can catch them on each band, you can build up an impressive total towards the Five-Band DXCC award very quickly.

One last reminder: Don't feel bad about being a casual participant in a contest. QSO-hungry contest stations rely on the thousands of part-time competitors who make only a few QSOs to rack up those impressive top-ten scores. If the contesters were limited to working only those stations who were really serious about the contest, they'd soon run out of stations to work. So go get 'em!

Chapter 13

DX Newsletters and Spotting Networks

A s a beginning DXer, one of the best investments you can make is a subscription to a DX newsletter. If your ultimate goal is the Honor Roll, you'll want to work every country that comes on the air. That means you have to know in advance when a DXpedition is planned and on what modes and frequencies they'll be operating.

DX newsletters also list DX stations heard or worked by readers who phone, fax or mail in their reports. These reports are extremely helpful in determining the operating habits of a DX stations you want to work. For example, you may need ZD9, Tristan da Cunha. In reading your bulletin you see that ZD9BV will be on Sunday afternoons on 28.478 MHz for three weeks running. Chances are, if you hang around 28.478 about that time, you'll run into him.

Another regular feature of the newsletters is an up-to-date listing of QSL managers. Each newsletter reflects its editor's interests and style, so you should write for samples (be sure to include return postage), then decide which one you like the best. I currently subscribe to two newsletters and find that they complement each other. The same information often appears in both, but the stations heard/worked information is usually not the same. All in all, a DX newsletter is an excellent value. Some newsletters advertise in the Ham-Ads Section of *QST*. See Table 13-1 for a list of several DX newsletters.

DX SPOTTING NETS

DX spotting nets are commonly found on VHF FM, sometimes on repeaters, sometimes simplex. Interested DXers can monitor the frequency with the squelch turned on. When a member hears a DX station that might be of interest to the others, he reports the call sign and frequency.

Some DX clubs sponsor weekly nets, where members meet and exchange information (translation: brag). There is a bit of posturing on these nets. You hear stations reporting countries you haven't even *heard,* saying, "Of course, at my level I don't need any of these, but I thought

Table 13-1

DX Newsletters

Here are some popular DX newsletters. For the latest subscription information, send an SASE to the listed address and ask for a sample copy.

QRZ DX
   PO Box 832205
   Richardson, TX 75083

THE DX BULLETIN
   PO Box 50
   Fulton, CA 95439

THE W6GO/K6HHD QSL MANAGER LIST
   PO Box 700
   Rio Linda, CA 95673-0700

---

somebody might be interested." There you sit, waiting for your turn, holding your list of new countries, and feeling pretty small. Well, *you* never worked them before and you have every reason to be proud of your accomplishment. Bear in mind, someone else will work that same station for the first time tomorrow. So read 'em off on the net. You might also resolve to not be so boastful when you hit the big time. DXers with a few years' experience may never bother to report many countries you need. Still, the chances are good that if a country gets reported by one of these "old-timers," you need it too. You could prepare a list of the countries you need and send it to the other users of the network, but you may wish to wait until you've pruned the list down a little!

DX PACKET NETWORKS

   DX packet networks are a logical outgrowth of VHF spotting nets. One advantage they have over voice nets is that they don't make any noise. Many users have a dedicated computer for this purpose; they need only keep an eye on the screen to see if anything they need has been reported. Packet spotting networks are usually on 2 meters, so you must have at least a Technician class license to *transmit*. Novices can monitor of course, but cannot "connect." To operate on packet, you need an FM transceiver, a personal computer (with terminal emulation software and a serial interface) or a terminal, and a "terminal-node controller" (TNC). For VHF packet-only operation, just about any TNC that uses the AX.25 level 2 protocol will work fine. You don't need a personal mailbox or any of the bells and whistles offered in the multimode controllers.

DX packet networks are usually based on the PacketCluster software, and many DXers find their totals climbing rapidly because of the advantages gained by regularly connecting to a Cluster node.

In the Northeast, when K1MM in the Boston area hears a DX station he thinks might be of interest, he enters the data through his local node. In less than a minute, every station monitoring the network (possibly the entire Northeast US!) knows about the DX.

In addition to listing the frequency and mode of on-the-air DX stations, PacketCluster can relay other detailed information, such as the station's operating habits, whether to use long or short path beam headings and so on.

PacketCluster also features a useful QSL-information data base. Let's say you've just worked S21DX and are eager to send him a QSL card. PacketCluster makes it as easy as possible. Simply invoke the "Show QSL" command and the Cluster will query the *W6GO/K6HHD QSL MANAGER LIST* data base (stored on-line) and attempt to provide you with the latest QSL route information. (This service is not available on all systems.)

PacketCluster can tell you sunrise and sunset times for any part of the world and provide beam headings to boot. The Cluster provides current WWV propagation information and access to other local data bases, such as FCC regulations, international postal requirements and QSL Bureau addresses.

Another function of PacketCluster is its bulletin board system, which operates in a way similar to conventional packet BBSs. Users can ask for help in locating a QSL route or solving a technical problem, or advertise personal equipment for sale or trade. Sending short informal messages to individual stations or the entire network is also possible. This feature is helpful when the pileup on a rare DX station is large. Someone who's already gotten through can act as a spotter, looking for the frequency on which the DX station is listening and listing it on the network. In addition to state-of-the-art DX reporting capabilities, PacketCluster has all the comforts of home! It's a real DXers' crystal ball.

Repeater and packet spotting nets are helpful in spotting unusual and rare stations, especially when they show up on a band where they are seldom heard. But most of the countries you'll work as part of your first 100 are on everyone else's first-100 list also, so they don't get listed very often. You may be tipped off to a somewhat rare station, but the pileup may take you an hour to crack. In that same time you might work three or four easier countries that you also need.

If you don't have a computer or a 2-meter radio, you're better off investing in a rotary beam and tower first. There's no sense hearing about stations you can't work! If you already have a good antenna system and a DX packet network is available to you, go ahead and use it. Of course, neither newsletters or gadgets can take the place of getting on the air and *listening*.

Chapter 14

The DX Century Club (DXCC)

D Xing was born in 1921 when US and Canadian amateurs first made contact with their peers in Europe, in "Trans-Atlantic Tests" sponsored by ARRL. It wasn't long before contacts were made between North America and Australia, Japan and South America. The League continued to foster the sport by reporting the call signs and favorite operating frequencies of the slowly increasing number of DX stations around the world. Sooner or later, it had to happen: DXers were comparing notes on how many countries each had *confirmed*, by letter or card, and the idea of an award for confirming contacts with 100 countries was born. The DX Century Club, sponsored from the beginning by ARRL, was formed in 1937. When only slightly more than 100 countries could boast of Amateur Radio activity, making DXCC was a lot tougher to achieve than it is now!

THE WORLD'S PREMIER DX AWARD

As the first DX award and the only one that recognizes contacts with political entities (rather than arbitrarily designated areas) worldwide, DXCC has maintained a prestige second to none for more than 50 years. Many other worthwhile DX awards are available, but DXCC is the undisputed leader.

As the name implies, membership in DXCC requires proof of contact with 100 different countries. With the exception of the Satellite DXCC Award, contacts made through amateur satellites or repeater stations don't count.

With these exceptions, all confirmed contacts you make from the same DXCC country can be submitted for DXCC. In other words, if you start DXing in Ohio, go the college in California, and settle in Connecticut, any contacts you made with your call sign(s) from these states are valid. Of course, the country you live in also counts toward DXCC. Don't forget this when you apply for the award!

Some DXCC "countries" are confusing at first. For example, the

48 contiguous United States, Alaska and Hawaii count as three separate countries. Alaska is considered a separate country because it is totally separated from the "lower 48" by Canada. Hawaii counts because of its distance from the mainland. So, if you start DXCC in California and later move to Alaska or Hawaii, you start over. If you ever move back to the mainland however, those earlier California contacts can be counted toward a "mainland DXCC."

There are many other unusual DXCC countries. Because of their distance from the mother country, or the presence of another country in between, several uninhabited, or occasionally or sparsely populated islands, reefs and atolls are also on the list. Some of them are barely accessible under the best weather conditions and rank high on DXers' "Most Wanted" lists.

The *DXCC Countries List* had to be greatly revised after the Second World War, which resulted in many boundary changes. The political world has certainly continued to evolve since 1945, as a glance at the "Deleted Countries" list will confirm. Examples of deleted countries are the former US Canal Zone in Panama, South Vietnam, Tibet and the former Karelo-Finnish Republic, now considered part of the Russian Republics. More than offsetting the deleted countries are the many countries that weren't on the list in 1945. They include Bouvet, Malyj-Visotskij, and Banaba islands, and Walvis Bay. The *DXCC Countries List* is as dynamic as the world we live in; new countries come on every couple of years, while others may be deleted.

MEMBERSHIP REQUIREMENTS

You can achieve several DXCCs, for different bands and modes. Almost everyone starts out with the Mixed award, meaning you can combine contacts made on CW and SSB, as well as RTTY (radio teletype), packet, AMTOR, or slow-scan television—whatever modes you operate. Contacts for the Mixed award may be made on any authorized amateur band except 30 meters.

Separate single-band awards are available for confirming 100 countries on 160, 80, 40, 10, 6, and 2 meters. In addition, you can apply for CW-only, Phone-only, RTTY and satellite DXCC awards. For the ambitious DXer, the Five-Band DXCC (5BDXCC) award recognizes those who have confirmed 100 countries each on 80, 40, 20, 15 and 10 meters. This award can be endorsed for confirming 100 countries on 160, 17, 12, 6 and 2 meters.

Except for 5BDXCC, all DXCC awards can be endorsed as your countries-confirmed total exceeds 100. A very special award called the

DXCC Honor Roll is also available, for Mixed, Phone, and CW. Achieving this distinction is absolutely the pinnacle of DX achievement. The number of confirmed countries necessary to make the Honor Roll depends on the mode and the number of current countries, but all require a confirmed total of over 300 countries! With so many countries available only once every decade or so, it takes many years of determined DXing to reach the Honor Roll.

DXCC applicants in the US must be ARRL members; Canadian applicants must belong to the CRRL (Canadian Radio Relay League).

In addition to return postage, there are registration and submission fees for DXCC. After the one-time registration fee, DXCC members who are also ARRL or CRRL members can make one submission per year at no charge. This submission can be for any number of DXCC awards, endorsements, or both. Additional submissions within the same calendar year require payment of an additional fee.

Non-League members outside the US and Canada are charged a fee for their first submission of any kind in each year, and an additional, greater fee for additional submissions in the same calendar year.

DXCC fees and return-postage costs are detailed in the application package, which is available from ARRL HQ.

HOW HARD IS IT TO CONFIRM 100 COUNTRIES?

Confirming 100 countries is easier than you think. If you apply the information contained in this book you'll work more than 100 countries before you know it.

Having a General class (or higher) license makes the task much easier, because many more opportunities are available, but hundreds of Novice and Technicians are DXCC members. Hams who casually operate for a few years, not passing up any DX they hear, but not particularly looking for any, either, can confirm 50-60 countries. That means they'll have to work for about the same number. There are hams who work more than 100 countries in a single contest weekend; you and I may not be in *that* league, but it shows what can be done and that there are many more than 100 active DXCC countries.

HOW DO I APPLY?

DXCC application forms and complete rules are available at no cost from ARRL HQ. When you write, enclose a dollar and ask for a copy of the ARRL *DXCC Countries List* as well. Chapter 4 explains how to use the *Countries List* to keep track of the countries you've worked and confirmed. There are two forms used for your first DXCC application. One is a typical information form. Note that you should list all call signs you have held that may appear on cards you're submitting for DXCC. If you aren't submitting cards from countries you confirmed from a previous call, you don't have to list them. On this form you have to indicate your ARRL membership number if you live in the US.

On the other form, you list the cards you are submitting. List them in the same order as they appear in the *DXCC Countries List*. With all the new prefixes in use nowadays, sorting them can be a problem! It won't be if you use the filing system recommended in Chapter 4. Each page of the application form has room for 55 entries; for your initial application, you'll need at least two pages. It's a good idea to submit a few extra countries with your initial application. Occasionally, for reasons discussed later in this chapter, a card is not acceptable for credit. If you submit cards for only 100 countries, you'll be asked to send another card. By sending confirmations for 102 or 103 countries, you may save some time.

Check each card carefully. Make sure your call sign was correctly entered by the DX station or manager. Any correction made to your call sign disqualifies the card. If you are applying for a mode-specific award, such as CW DXCC, every card must indicate that CW was the mode.

The QSL card does not have to state two-way CW, but a cross-mode contact doesn't count. A cross-mode contact means one station was on CW, let's say, and the other was on SSB. Remember, corrections made to the card will lead to its disqualification. Don't make them! If you have a doubt about a card and it's the only one you have from that country, submit it anyway and let the DXCC officials decide. But, if it's your first DXCC application for that mode, be sure to send at least one extra card in case it doesn't qualify.

Once you have all the forms filled out and the cards sorted, wrap them carefully and send them to the DXCC Administrator at ARRL Headquarters. Letting go of more than 100 hard-won QSL cards is a traumatic experience. Wrap them carefully and make sure the addresses are legible. With your application, you'll receive a card that tells you the approximate return postage costs you should include with your application.

Each card submitted for DXCC is inspected by the DXCC Administrator and an assistant. Once checked, your cards are returned, along with another form telling you how many cards you were credited with, and the reasons for any rejections. Save this form, as you must include it when you apply to endorse your basic award. Finally, the big day comes and your certificate arrives in the mail. Buy an attractive frame and display your certificate proudly. You earned it!

ENDORSEMENTS

DXCC awards can be endorsed for additional countries worked. If you have fewer than 250 countries confirmed, you can submit cards in increments of 25, at any time. When you have more than 250 countries confirmed, you can submit 10 cards at a time. Honor Roll members can submit one or more cards at any time. Once a year, any DXCC member can submit any number of cards, regardless of the number of countries he has confirmed. For example, if you have 250 countries confirmed in Newington, and haven't submitted cards in a year or more, you can send in fewer than 10 cards. You won't receive an endorsement sticker until you get to 260, but your records will be updated, and the DXCC listing in *QST* will show your new total.

SINGLE-BAND DXCC

Single-band DXCC is available for contacts made on 160, 80, 40, 10, 6 and 2 meters. Ten-meter DXCC is within the grasp of any Novice or Technician with even a modest SSB station. Many amateurs are very serious about single-band DXCC. Countries-worked totals achieved on one band by some stations make even us multiband, mixed-mode DXers green with envy!

QSL FIELD CHECKING

You can have the QSLs for your first DXCC checked by an authorized DXCC "Field Checker," instead of sending them to ARRL HQ. Right now this service is only available in the US. Field Checkers are experienced DXers appointed by ARRL, who volunteer to check cards at hamfests and conventions. Cards for certain rare countries must still be checked at HQ. Full details on the Field Checking program are included in the *DXCC Countries List*.

Chapter 15

Beyond DXCC

Y
ou may be very close to working 100 countries, or have already reached that magic number. If so, congratulations! You generally won't be working five or six new countries at a session anymore, but new ones will still come along with surprising regularity. Of course, as you work more and more countries, new ones are harder to find. Pay careful attention to each week's newsletter to see if anything you need is on the air or is expected soon. If you've become a *serious* DXer, you want to work *every* DXpedition that comes on the air. DX newsletters are your best source of information on upcoming DXpeditions.

By now, you should have a good idea of the strengths and weaknesses of your station, and you'll no doubt be thinking of improvements. The biggest improvement I made was to label all the tuning knobs on my antenna tuners and amplifier, so I can change bands in seconds. Late one night I was having a last look at 40 meters before hitting the sack. The QRN was pretty bad, but it was about sunrise time in Africa and the Middle East. My amplifier was turned off, and as luck would have it, it was tuned for 20 meters. The weak signal calling CQ turned out to be Z21CA, in Zimbabwe, a country I needed on 40! I simply flipped the band switch and reset the tuning knobs to the positions marked on the piece of white cardboard inserted behind them. When Z21CA signed, I was able to give my standard ×1 call (I sign my call once) and I worked him on that call. The pileup after my QSO was fierce, and he only worked one more station before going "QRT for breakfast." I haven't heard a Z2 on 40 CW since.

When you have worked just about every country that's currently on the air, satisfaction comes in other ways. I checked 20 meters the other night. Conditions were terrible. At about 14.022 I turned up a pileup of US stations. After a few minutes of looking, in amongst the auroral buzzing, static crashes, and QRM, I could hear a station passing out fast reports. A few East Coast stations were getting through. At last I was able to copy his call and discovered it was a T32 (Eastern Kiribati/Line

Glossary of Terms

Terminator—The "line" on the globe that separates the daytime and night-time regions of the earth.

Islands), a country I already have confirmed on 20 CW. It was a great relief to be able to shut down the rig and go to bed!

OTHER GOALS

The pinnacle of DXing is the DXCC Honor Roll. Requirements for the Honor Roll are given in the Countries List, so I won't repeat them. It takes many years to work all the countries you need to make the Honor Roll, so you'll need other goals in the meantime. When the solar cycle is at its peak, you can work Five-Band DXCC (5BDXCC) in a surprisingly short time.

10 METERS

If you think you want to work 5BDXCC, and solar conditions are favorable, concentrate first on 10 meters. This band is the first to suffer as the sunspot cycle declines, so get 'em while you can! You can work most of the 100 you need in one DX-contest weekend. Because there is less ionospheric absorption on 10 meters, low-power signals tend to be stronger than on the lower bands. Notice how loud the 10- and 25-watt mobile stations are and you'll see what I mean. When the solar flux is greater than 200, you can work 100 countries on 10 meters from anywhere in the US running 100 W to a vertical antenna.

80 METERS

Eighty meters is the hardest HF band on which to work 100 countries. Effective 80-meter DX antennas are harder to install than their counterparts on the higher bands, and there is less DX activity on the band. Because of ionospheric absorption, signal strengths are usually lower, and the QRN can be murder! Another problem on 80 meters is the strength of short-skip (under 1000 miles) and local signals. QRM is thus more of a problem on 80 than on the higher bands. Added to the amateur QRM is that from nonamateur signals coming from who knows where. Some of the garbage that passes for radio emission from these so-called professional stations has to be heard to be believed, and hear it you will! Low-noise directional receiving antennas (Beverages if you have room, loops if you don't), are a must. Eighty meters is especially sensitive to the terminator effect, the strengthening of signals at sunrise and sunset on one or both ends of the path.

When I hear one of these countries on 40, I ask the station to QSY or set up a schedule (sked). This technique has brought me a handful of new ones on 80 meters. If you set up a sked, make sure the time is right for you. High noon local time in the US is not a good time for a sked with India on 80 meters!

TRY ANOTHER BAND

Another way to remain active while you wait for the next new one is to explore the bands you don't normally use for DXing, such as 160 and 6 meters and the WARC bands. QSOs on any band count for CW, Phone and Mixed DXCC, and 5BDXCC is endorsable for 12, 17 and 160 meters. The WARC bands haven't really been discovered yet and pileups are much less intimidating.

By the way, many older HF power amplifiers will work fine on 12 and 17 meters. I use my old Heathkit SB-220 by setting the band switch to 10 meters for 24 MHz, and 15 meters for 18 MHz. Apply drive and tune up slowly at first, in case the plate RF choke resonates on a WARC band, as is sometimes the case. Of course, for US stations, the power limit on the 30-meter band is 200 W out.

AWARDS

The ARRL Operating Manual describes many interesting domestic and foreign awards you can work for while progressing toward the Honor Roll. One is the *CQ* Worked All Zones (WAZ) award, which dates back nearly as far as DXCC. The 40 zones were established before the Second World War, but their boundaries are anything but arbitrary. It is quite possible to have worked over 200 countries and not have worked all 40 zones!

The Worked All Europe (WAE) award, offered in three levels, will get you working Europeans on several bands to get the necessary points. WAE has some historical interest, as the sponsor (Deutscher Amateur Radio Club, DARC) counts some regions as "countries" that have been absorbed by other political bodies. One example is the region of Russia called Karelia, which counts as the Karelo-Finnish Republic for WAE. Russian stations with UA1N or UZ1N prefixes are located in this region. Working for these awards may lead you to a deeper study of history and international politics. You may even decide to learn to speak one or more foreign languages, which you can try out on the air.

IOTA (Islands on the Air)

You probably learned in school that two-thirds of the earth's surface is covered with water. Thus, it's no surprise that our planet is dotted with uncounted thousands of islands. Many islands, such as Puerto Rico, Cuba, Bouvet, Peter I and Kerguelen, count as separate countries for DXCC. However, there are still thousands of islands that count only as parts of some larger country or island chain for that award.

Some years ago, Geoff Watts, a British shortwave listener, came up with the IOTA award to stimulate interest in working stations on all those other islands. Later, the ARRL's sister society in the UK, the Radio Society of Great Britain (RSGB), assumed responsibility for administering the IOTA award. IOTA islands are identified by distinctive letter-and-number codes, such as NA-42, AF-26, OC-51 and so on. The letters indicate the continental group to which the island is assigned. Every identified island within a continental group is assigned a serial number, which follows the continental group letters.

The basic IOTA award requires that you contact 100 IOTA islands. Like DXCC, endorsements are given for additional islands beyond 100. The IOTA list is extensive, and constantly growing as islands are added. Because the number of islands is so vast, it is unlikely that anyone will ever work them all! Write to the RSGB for additional information.

One benefit of the IOTA program is the training it provides for DXers and those who like to be the DX. North America alone provides dozens of opportunities for IOTA DXpeditions. IOTA pileups are not quite as fierce as those for rare DXCC countries, but the program is gaining in popularity. Soon, it may be difficult to tell the difference. When there's nothing new on the bands, DXers get itchy for a pileup, and a new IOTA island often provides the cure.

Even if you haven't caught the IOTA bug, an IOTA pileup gives you an excellent opportunity to sharpen your skills, without the pressure of needing the QSO for a new DXCC country.

IOTA nets meet every Saturday on 14260 kHz at 1300 UTC and every Sunday on 21300 kHz, also at 1300 UTC.

DXING ON OTHER MODES

Radio amateurs like to work DX, no matter what mode they're operating. On the HF bands, you might like to try slow-scan TV (SSTV), radio teletype (RTTY) or its cousins, packet and AMTOR. Contacts made on these modes count for Mixed DXCC.

If you have a Technician license, you might be interested in satellite

DXing. Amateur satellites are repeaters, with inputs and outputs on different bands. Typical satellite stations are capable of operating on the 2-meter, 70-cm and 23-cm bands, SSB and CW. There is a separate DXCC award for satellite contacts. Because they are made through a repeater, these contacts don't count for other DXCC awards.

During periods of high solar activity, the 6-meter band is often open for international DXing. Until recently, far fewer countries authorized their radio amateurs to operate on 6 meters, but that is rapidly changing. VHF DXing is not limited to 6 meters, though. Since the 1950s, hams have been communicating on VHF by bouncing signals off earth's first satellite, the moon. Called EME (for earth-moon-earth) communication, this fascinating mode has progressed from the laboratory to the point where an entire station can be assembled from store-bought equipment. You don't need gigantic antennas and lots of power; there are enough big stations operating all over the world to give the little guns plenty of activity.

Because the moon is a *passive* reflector, not a repeater, EME contacts count for the traditional DXCC awards. In addition, there are separate DXCC awards for the VHF and UHF bands.

The ARRL Handbook and the *Operating Manual* are the best places to find information about these modes.

A CHANGE OF SCENERY

If none of these suggestions appeals to you, you've been looking at the same walls for too long. You could rearrange your shack, or you can just get out of it for a while. On a mid-winter visit to Florida, I took my transceiver and a 40-meter wire ground plane, which I put up in a tree. I made a point of working 40 CW during the "terminators," sunrise and sunset, which were at slightly different times than in the Northeast. Learning about propagation conditions from this location 1500 miles from home gave my interest in DXing a real lift, and I even worked 3B8CF for a new one on 40! Of course, if you're really feeling the blahs, you could leave the country altogether and be on the other side of the pileup!

DX VACATIONS

There are dozens of vacation/DXpedition opportunities available to the North American radio amateur. The Caribbean islands alone offer many DXCC countries, most of which issue reciprocal licenses at reasonable fees. ARRL HQ has licensing information for every country for which US amateurs can obtain operating permission. A travel agent can help with reservations and transportation. Now all you need is some information on operating as a DX station.

Casual or Serious Operation?

Nothing is more frustrating to the avid DXer than hearing a DX station who prefers casual operation to slinging out the contacts. Casual operation overseas is not much different than at home, except you can expect to have more stations calling you! But you can operate casually at home. As long as you're in some faraway place, why not work as many stations as you can?

Handling the Pileup: Who's in Charge Here?

Unfortunately, many part-time DX stations (and even some full-time ones) run for cover when they attract a pileup. Heck, the pileup is the best part! The anxiety should be on the side of those calling you. All you have to do is pick out calls and hand out reports! You don't have to worry about working one station or another, but everyone in your pileup has a real *need* to work you! About the only mistake you can make is to miscopy someone's call. Don't worry: He'll let you know! Remember, you are in charge. Don't let a rowdy pileup scare you; take control. If someone calls out of turn or tries to break in, don't work him. When you are trying to work one station and others are calling at the same time, politely insist they stand by while you get the call and report. Remember, it's your party. You called a particular station and you have a right to work that station before any other. Don't let one or two bullies take over.

Work Split

Working split spreads out the pileup and makes it easier to hear individual calls. Traditionally, DX stations listen above their transmitting frequency. When you are working split, you must *never* work a station that calls on your transmitting frequency. If you do, the pack will move to that frequency and no one will ever hear you again! Announce the range of frequencies you're listening on and stick to it. For example: "This is KR1S/C6A, listening fourteen two-hundred to fourteen two-ten."

By the Numbers

Some DX stations work by call areas, accepting only calls from stations in the announced area. This method can lead to some problems. The FCC no longer issues a new call sign when you move to a different call area. WB2CHO lives in California, K5NA lives in New York and KH6CP lives in Connecticut. When propagation favors the East Coast, you'll ignore KH6CP's call; when you're working the West Coast long path and listening for "W sixes," you'll ignore WB2CHO. K5NA gets cheated on both ends! If you accept "portable" calls, you'll be absolutely amazed at how quickly hams move around the country!

Another problem with working by call areas is demographics. If you spend an equal amount of time working first-call-area stations as you spend on the fourth call area, the fours are denied an equivalent proportion of your attention, as they outnumber the ones. Finally, going by call areas keeps all the areas except the one you're working on hold, raising blood pressures and boring the on-hold DXers out of their minds. Spending an hour listening to other call areas getting contacts while you wait for your turn is very tedious. Unless you are in a very rare country, working split should allow you to pick out calls without resorting to "going by the numbers."

DX stations usually operate by call areas to "give everyone a chance." It's nice to be fair, but DXing is *competition*, after all. Besides, there's no point in listening for call areas to which you have no propagation. If you want to give everyone a chance, study the propagation and operate at times when it's favorable to different parts of the country. The propagation charts in *QST* and the *ARRL Operating Manual* can help you determine the best times and bands for propagation to different parts of North America.

If, after all, you decide to go by call areas, here are some more tips. Don't spend too much time on each call area. If you keep moving along, nobody has to wait long for another shot at you. It's not too bad spending an hour or so in a pileup for a new one if you're kept busy. Waiting an hour to have a five-minute chance to get through is irritating!

Taking a List

Some inexperienced DX operators who don't work split take their own lists. They stand by for a couple of minutes while the pack howls, writing down whatever parts of calls they hear. Then they work the stations on their list before taking another one. Unless you have a commanding signal, this method causes trouble also. While the pack is calling, you can be sure no one will try to operate on your frequency. But, while you're working stations, your frequency is quieter. If you take your own list, you can be sure that stations not on the list will call you. They may not realize you are taking a list, or they may hope to get lucky. If you work one station not on your list, you can expect to lose control immediately. You've changed the rules and everyone will start calling again. Unless you're in a pretty rare place, however, you can probably maintain a good QSO rate without taking a list.

One of the offshoots of list operations is the "last two letters" phenomenon. You're better off asking for complete call signs. You may not always be able to copy a complete call sign every time. With practice, though, you can usually get most of the call, most of the time. Using the last-two-letters method adds at least 30 percent to your time per contact, and may even double it. When you respond to the last two letters, more often than not, several stations will call. You pick one out and call him, and try to get the full call. Finally, after two or three transmissions, you get a complete contact. If you get all or most of the call the first time, however, you save at least one transmission. Just say, "No partial calls."

If you are operating from a rare or semirare country, the word quickly gets around. It's an unnecessary waste of time to repeat your name, location and QSL route for every contact. Every five minutes is often enough. You can be sure that anyone who needs a QSL card knows who and where you are and will hang around to get the QSL information. In fact, many of them will already have all the information, especially if you notified one or two DX newsletters of your planned operation. Just give the other station's call sign and a signal report. Listen to make sure you copied the call correctly and get your report. If you're unsure of a call, ask the station to repeat it. If you make a mistake in copying a call, repeat the correct call so the DXer knows you got it right. If more DX stations did this, there would be far fewer "insurance" contacts, and tidier pileups. The longer you spend on each contact, the bigger your pileup gets and the harder it will be for you to pick out calls. If you work two or more stations a minute, you can keep the pileup manageable, which is better for everyone. The best way to control a pileup is to work every station in it.

Nets

If you don't think your signal is strong enough to control a frequency, or you just don't want to deal with a pileup, you may wish to check into one of the many DX nets. Your QSO rate won't be as high, but neither will your blood pressure! But, don't be afraid to try a little freestyle operating, too. It's a whole lot easier from the DX end; remember, you're in charge.

Modes

At home, you may prefer either phone or CW. While you're away, why not try both? This is a good way to give everyone a chance to work you. Even if your code speed won't get you into the record books, don't worry. Transmit at the speed you can comfortably copy and work the stations that get the hint and slow down. Working CW is useful when someone's sleeping or relaxing in the same room because it's quiet. Playing CW DX station is also an excellent way to increase your speed if you're thinking about upgrading. By the way, don't forget the Novice/Technician subbands, especially if you're a little rusty on CW.

Working phone can be a pleasant way to spend a hot afternoon in the tropics. Try not to let your microphone pick up the sound of waves breaking on the dazzling white beach or the native band serenading you from the courtyard—we're already jealous enough.

Your Schedule

If you're combining a vacation or business trip with your DXpedition, you may not want to be tied down to a schedule. Depending on how rare your location is, though, following even a loose schedule is the most humane way to deal with the DXers who need you. Your early appearances will be noted on packet networks and in DX newsletters, and the needy will try to find you at the same times and frequencies. If you are at least on the air at about the same time each day, the DX sentries will find you. In fact, if your country is rare enough, they'll stay up all night and even take days off from work or school if they think the odds are good you'll show up at a certain time on a band where propagation is favorable.

Logging

Keeping an adequate log is not difficult. Most DXpeditions use some form of notebook rather than printed log sheets or books. You needn't log the actual time of each contact; just note the time every 10-15 minutes. At the top of each page, note the date, band, and mode (SSB, CW, packet, RTTY and so on). When you change bands or modes, start a new page. You can list calls in two or more columns to save space. While you're operating, you only have to enter the call of the station for each contact. Even if you are given a name and QTH, you needn't enter that information: It will appear on the station's QSL card.

QSL Cards

The job isn't finished until the paperwork is filled out! If your trip is longer than a week, you'll have QSLs waiting for you when you get home. US hams *should* send you a self-addressed, stamped envelope at the very least; overseas hams will probably send IRCs or green stamps. You can be your own manager, or you can look for someone to handle the job for you. Or, you can contact one of the well-known QSL managers listed in *QST* and the DX newsletters.

If you decide to do the job yourself, sort the cards you receive in order of date and time of contact. Then, you can zip through your log, confirming each in turn.

Whatever coping mechanisms you adopt, keep in mind that new countries eventually come along, as sure as the sun comes up, if not as predictably. One of the great attributes of Amateur Radio is its diversity, and the motivated ham should never want for new experiences. Of one thing I can assure you: Once a DXer, always a DXer! No matter where in the spectrum you venture, you'll always find your way back to the usual DX frequencies.

See you there!

REFERENCES AND SUGGESTED READING

Operating and General Information

Devoldere, *Antennas and Techniques for Low-Band DXing*, 2nd ed. (Newington: ARRL, 1993).

Eckersley, *Amateur Radio Operating Manual* (Hertfordshire, England: RSGB, 1985) (available from ARRL).

Ford, ed., *The ARRL Operating Manual* (Newington: ARRL, 1991).

Ford, ed., *Your Packet Companion* (Newington: ARRL, 1992).

Schetgen, ed., *The ARRL Handbook* (Newington: ARRL). Published annually.

Locher, *The Complete DX'er* (Deerfield, Illinois: Idiom Press, 2nd ed., 1989).

Palm, ed., *The FCC Rule Book* (Newington: ARRL, 1993).

The ARRL DXCC Countries List (Newington: ARRL). Updated regularly.

Propagation

Jacobs and Cohen, *The Shortwave Propagation Handbook*, 2nd ed. (CQ Publishing, 1982).

Rosenthal and Hirman, *A Radio Frequency User's Guide to the Space Environment Services Center Geophysical Alert Broadcasts* (Boulder, CO: NOAA, 1990).

Antennas

DeMaw, *W1FB's Antenna Notebook* (Newington: ARRL, 1987).

Hall, ed., *The ARRL Antenna Book* (Newington: ARRL, 16th ed., 1991).

Hall, ed., *The ARRL Antenna Compendium, Vol 1* (Newington: ARRL, 1985).

Hall, ed., *The ARRL Antenna Compendium, Vol 2* (Newington: ARRL, 1989).

Hall, ed., *The ARRL Antenna Compendium, Vol 3* (Newington: ARRL, 1992).

Heys, *Practical Wire Antennas* (Hertfordshire, England: RSGB, 1989) (available from ARRL).

Lawson, *Yagi Antenna Design* (Newington: ARRL, 1986).

Moxon, *HF Antennas for All Locations*, 2nd ed. (Hertfordshire, England: RSGB, 1993). (available from ARRL).

ABOUT THE AUTHOR

Jim Kearman, KR1S, was first licensed as WN2EDW in 1962. He obtained his Extra Class license in 1974. From 1976 to 1978, he worked at ARRL HQ, first in the Communications Department and later as an Assistant Technical Editor.

With Chod Harris, WB2CHO, he coauthored *OSCAR—From the Ground Up*. He also edited the second edition of *FM and Repeaters for the Radio Amateur*. Jim returned to ARRL HQ in 1991. His most recent book is *Low Profile Amateur Radio*.

Return this coupon* with your next purchase of $5 or more and we'll send you a free DXCC Countries List.

*Limit one coupon per purchase

THE DXCC
COMPANION

FEEDBACK

Please use this form to give us your comments on this book and what you'd like to see in future editions.

Where did you purchase this book? □ From ARRL directly □ From an ARRL dealer

Is there a dealer who carries
ARRL publications within: □ 5 miles □ 15 miles □ 30 miles of your location? □ Not sure.

License class:
□ Novice □ Technician □ Technician with HF privileges
□ General □ Advanced □ Extra

Name _____ Call sign _____

Address _____

City, State/Province, ZIP/Postal Code _____

Daytime Phone ( ) _____ Age_____

Licensed, how long?_____ ARRL member? □ Yes □ No

Other hobbies_____

_____

Occupation _____

From _____

_____

_____

EDITOR, THE DXCC COMPANION
AMERICAN RADIO RELAY LEAGUE
225 MAIN ST
NEWINGTON CT 06111-1494

··· please fold and tape ······························